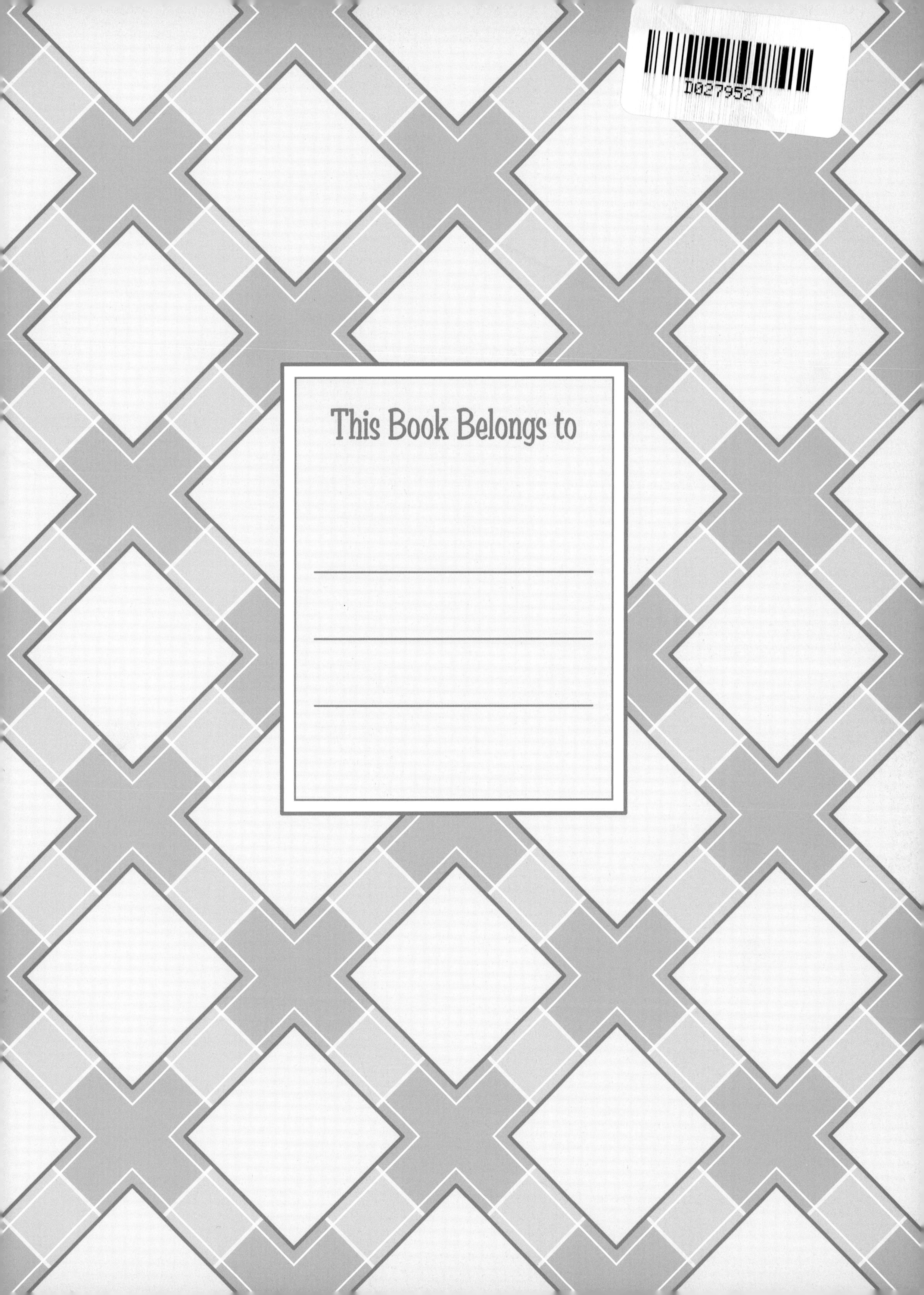
This Book Belongs to

THE SIMPSONS 2012 ANNUAL

For information address
Bongo Comics Group
P.O. Box 1963, Santa Monica, CA 90406-1963

Published in the UK by Titan Books, a division of Titan Publishing Group,
144 Southwark St., London SE1 0UP, under licence from Bongo Entertainment, Inc.

FIRST EDITION: AUGUST 2011

ISBN: 9780857685278

3 5 7 9 10 8 6 4 2

Publisher: Matt Groening
Creative Director: Bill Morrison
Managing Editor: Terry Delegeane
Director of Operations: Robert Zaugh
Art Director: Nathan Kane
Art Director Special Projects: Serban Cristescu
Production Manager: Christopher Ungar
Assistant Art Director: Chia-Hsien Jason Ho
Production/Design: Karen Bates, Nathan Hamill, Art Villanueva
Staff Artist: Mike Rote
Administration: Ruth Waytz, Pete Benson
Legal Guardian: Susan A. Grode

PRINTED IN ITALY

ANNUAL 2012

TITAN BOOKS

PAT MCGREAL SCRIPT · ***JAMES LLOYD*** PENCILS · ***ANDREW PEPOY*** INKS · ***ART VILLANUEVA*** COLORS · ***KAREN BATES*** LETTERS · ***BILL MORRISON*** EDITOR

TWO MINUTES LATER...
AAAAIIIEEEEE!
YAAARRRRGH!
FUH-WHUMMP!
THANKS, MOE. I CAN WALK FROM HERE.
HOLD ON A MINUTE! HELP ME HAUL THIS SCRAP-HEAP OUTTA THE DRIFT!
HUNGH! HURF! GRUNT!
SAY! THE MOONLIGHT IS GLINTIN' OFFA SOMETHING BRIGHT AND SHINY IN THEM TREES!
I HAFTA FIND OUT WHAT IT IS! I'M LIKE A MAGPIE THAT WAY!
...OR A VULTURE.

WHOA! A LITTLE CARGO PLANE! HOPE NO ONE'S HURT! I HATE BLOOD AND WHINING!
EMPTY! THE PILOT MUSTA BAILED! C'MON! LET'S SEE WHAT'S INSIDE!
37
THERE'S NOTHING IN HERE BUT A BUNCH OF BARRELS!
WHAT IS THIS?
TOP SECRET SAUCE
YOWZA! INDESCRIBABLY DELICIOUS! AND IT'S ALL MINE!
BUT, MOE! THIS STUFF BELONGS TO SOMEBODY!
DON'T BE A NINNY! LOAD THE GOODS INTO THE CAR!
SWEET SERENDIPITY! THAT SAUCE AND MY HORSE-MEAT MIGHT BE A MATCH MADE IN HEAVEN!
GRUNT! NGH! HURF!

BACK AT THE BAR...
THERE! I SLATHERED THIS PATTY WITH THE GLOP! HAVE A TASTE!
DON'T GET YOUR HOPES UP, MOE. YOUR BURGERS ARE RANK!
LADIES NIGHT TUESDAY
CHOMP!
...URK...
AHHHH... GLURRG...YUMMMM...
THE **BEST** BURGER IN THE WORLD! EVER! HANDS DOWN! **GIMME ANOTHER!!**
YES! THIS SAUCE'LL DRAW CUSTOMERS LIKE FLIES TO DOGGY DOO! I'LL MAKE PILES OF DOUGH!
DON'T TELL NOBODY ABOUT WHAT WE FOUND, HOMER! **NOBODY!** THIS IS OUR SECRET...**SAUCE!**

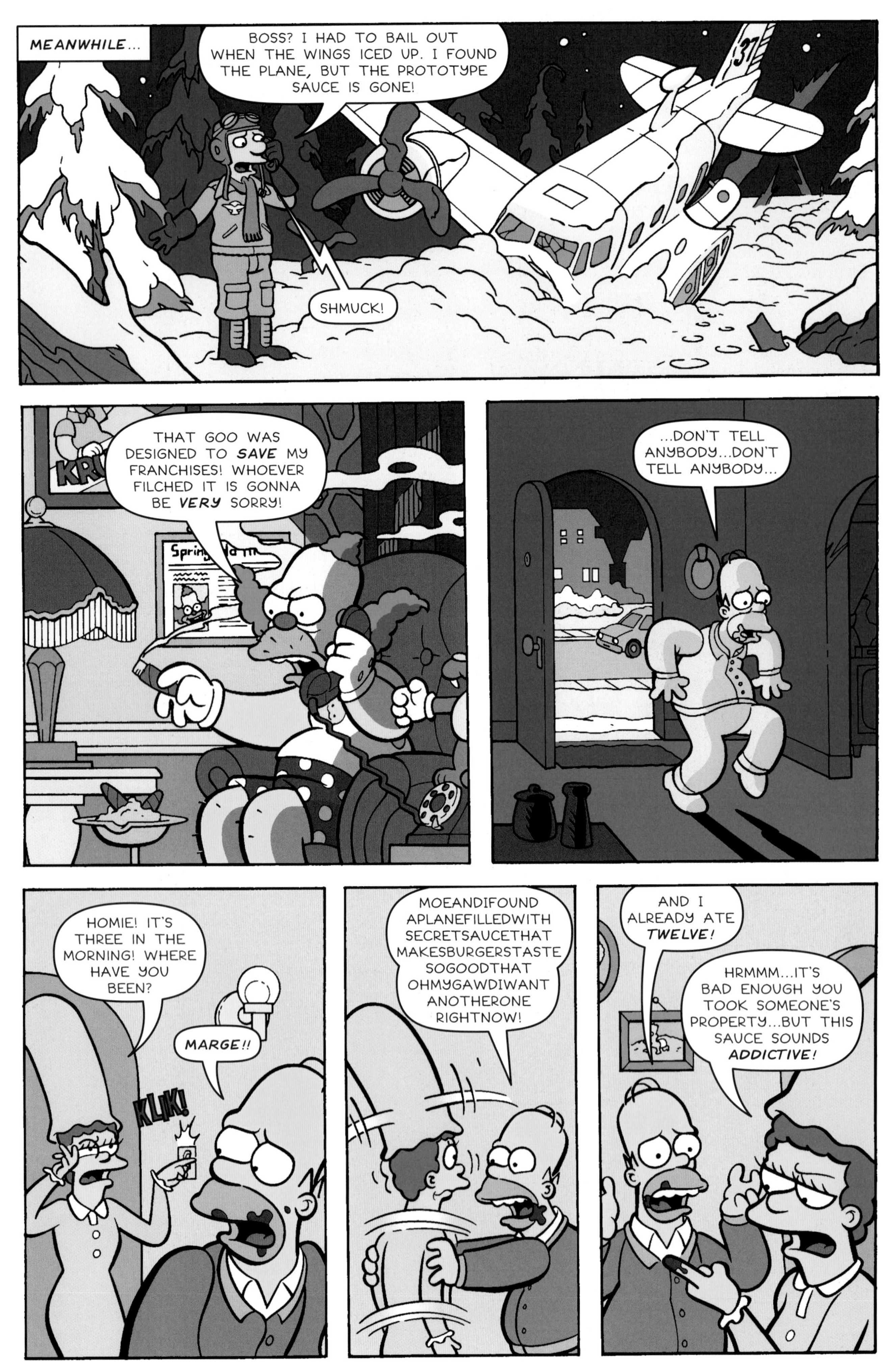
MEANWHILE...
BOSS? I HAD TO BAIL OUT WHEN THE WINGS ICED UP. I FOUND THE PLANE, BUT THE PROTOTYPE SAUCE IS GONE!
SHMUCK!
THAT GOO WAS DESIGNED TO SAVE MY FRANCHISES! WHOEVER FILCHED IT IS GONNA BE VERY SORRY!
...DON'T TELL ANYBODY...DON'T TELL ANYBODY...
HOMIE! IT'S THREE IN THE MORNING! WHERE HAVE YOU BEEN?
KLIK!
MARGE!!
MOEANDIFOUND APLANEFILLEDWITH SECRETSAUCETHAT MAKESBURGERSTASTE SOGOODTHAT OHMYGAWDIWANT ANOTHERONE RIGHTNOW!
AND I ALREADY ATE TWELVE!
HRMMM...IT'S BAD ENOUGH YOU TOOK SOMEONE'S PROPERTY...BUT THIS SAUCE SOUNDS ADDICTIVE!

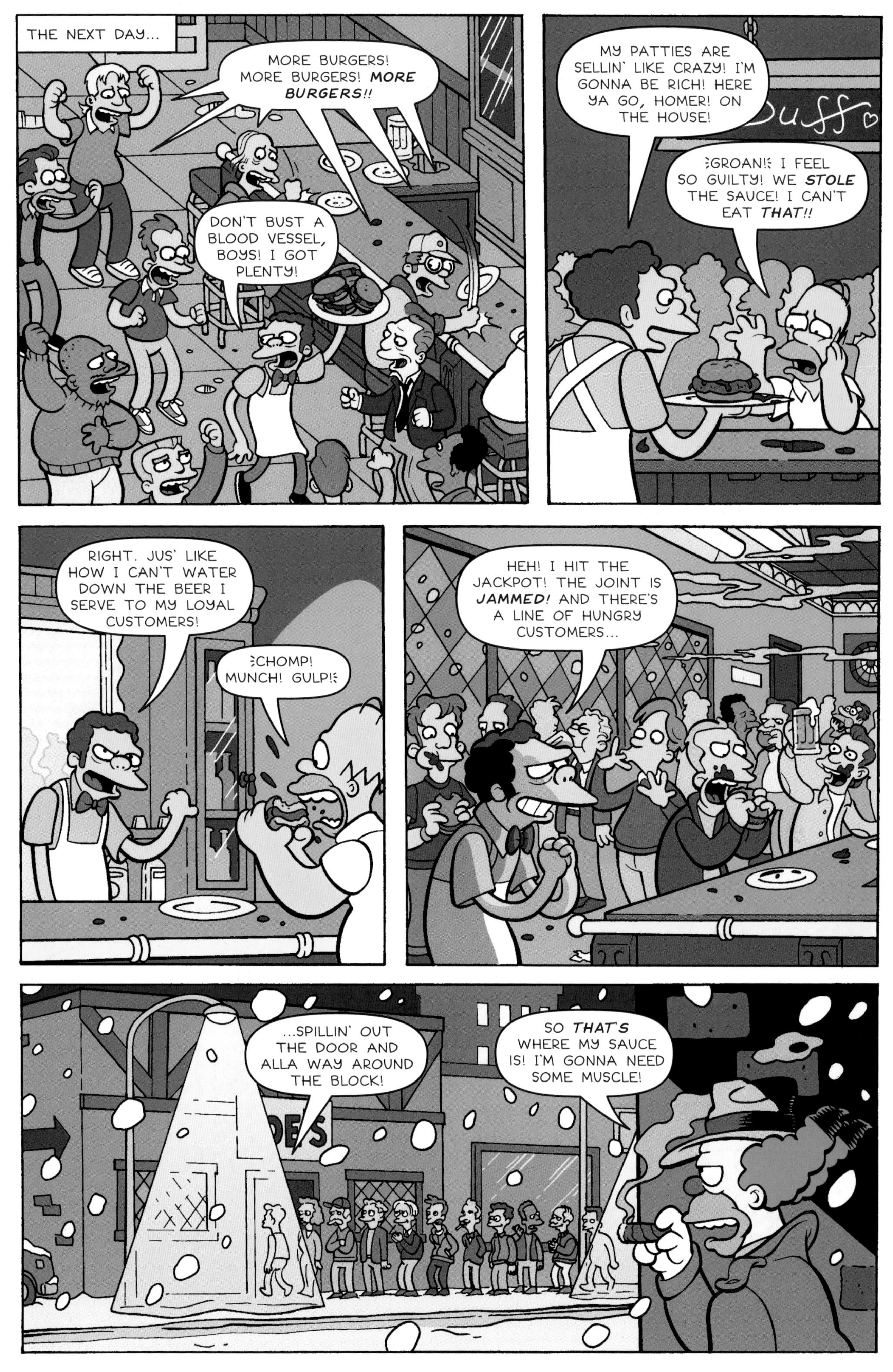
THE NEXT DAY...
MORE BURGERS! MORE BURGERS! MORE BURGERS!!
DON'T BUST A BLOOD VESSEL, BOYS! I GOT PLENTY!
MY PATTIES ARE SELLIN' LIKE CRAZY! I'M GONNA BE RICH! HERE YA GO, HOMER! ON THE HOUSE!
Duff
GROAN! I FEEL SO GUILTY! WE STOLE THE SAUCE! I CAN'T EAT THAT!!
RIGHT. JUS' LIKE HOW I CAN'T WATER DOWN THE BEER I SERVE TO MY LOYAL CUSTOMERS!
CHOMP! MUNCH! GULP!
HEH! I HIT THE JACKPOT! THE JOINT IS JAMMED! AND THERE'S A LINE OF HUNGRY CUSTOMERS...
...SPILLIN' OUT THE DOOR AND ALLA WAY AROUND THE BLOCK!
SO THAT'S WHERE MY SAUCE IS! I'M GONNA NEED SOME MUSCLE!

ELSEWHERE...
I WANT THIS SPECK OF SAUCE ANALYZED, PROFESSOR FRINK!
POTRZEBIE, PRETTY LADY!
THIS MESHUGENAH BARKEEP, FAT TONY...HE'S GOT MY SECRET SAUCE. BWAAH! I DON'T KNOW WHAT TO DO!
"I DON'T KNOW WHAT TO DO! I DON'T KNOW WHAT TO DO!" BOO HOO HOO!
YOU CAN ACT LIKE A CLOWN, THAT'S WHAT YOU CAN DO! WHAT'S THE MATTER WITH YOU?
SMEK!
IS THIS HOW YOU ENTERTAIN THE CHILDREN?! BY CRYING LIKE A WOMAN?!
SNIFF! SNUK! NO, FAT TONY.
YOU LOOK TERRIBLE! RELAX! I'LL GET YOU YOUR SAUCE... PROVIDED I GET TO DIP MY BEAK IN THE KRUSTYBURGER FRANCHISE!

HEY, HOMER! WHAT'S WITH THE BLOTCHY SPOTS AND WARTY SKIN-TAGS? YOU'RE COVERED WITH 'EM!
SO ARE YOU! WHO CARES? MORE BURGERS, BARKEEP!
INNA MINUTE! I'M COUNTIN' SWEET GREENBACKS!
WHEN YOU'RE FINISHED, HAND 'EM OVER, SZYSLAK!
ULP! FAT TONY!
MY SAUCE! GET MY SAUCE!
YOU HEARD THE CLOWN, BOYS! TURN THIS DUMP UPSIDE DOWN! TAKE IT ALL...THE DOUGH, THE GOO, AND THE BURGERS!
RRRRRR! MINE!
YOIKS!
BUZZ OFF! YOU DON'T SCARE ME!
NO? IT WOULD BEHOOVE YOU TO RECONSIDER! ELSE YOU MAY FIND YOURSELF A CONTESTANT IN A LITTLE GAME WE CALL "YOU BET YOUR KNEECAPS"!

I...UH...GET YER DRIFT! YOU WIN! FAIR AN' SQUARE! PLEASE! SAMPLE YOUR CONQUEST!
GOOD IDEA! LET'S SEE WHAT THIS GLOP IS ALL ABOUT!
OY!
MAMA MIA!
WOW!
THAT'S IT! GOBBLE 'EM UP, GENTS! THERE'S PLENTY MORE!
MMMMM! CHOMP! MUNCH!
GASP! MOE!
I THINK YOU'LL FIND THAT TASTY SAUCE PACKS QUITE A WALLOP!
DROP THOSE BURGERS!
I HAD THE SAUCE ANALYZED! IT'S IN VIOLATION OF EVERY FDA REGULATION! THE STUFF IS TOXIC!
JUST LOOK AT WHAT IT'S DOING TO MY HOMIE!
WHAT?! I'M FINE!

THIS WILL HAPPEN TO EVERYONE WHO EATS IT!
PATOOIE!
WE GOTTA DEEP SIX THAT SAUCE BEFORE THE FEDS GET WISE!
AT THE SPRINGFIELD RIVER...
YOUR SKIN IS CLEARING UP, HOMIE! THANK GOODNESS I ARRIVED IN TIME!
SNIFF! I'LL MISS THOSE YUMMY BURGERS!
THERE! THAT'S THE LAST OF THE GLOP! LET'S SCRAM!
SPLASH!
SPLOOSH!
SLURP! SLURP! SLURP!
IT SURE CAN'T DO ANY HARM AT THE BOTTOM OF THE DRINK!
BOINK!
THE END

FREEZER BURNS
AND NOW, WITH FURTHER PROOF THAT THIS IS THE COLDEST WINTER IN SPRINGFIELD HISTORY, OUR OWN CHANNEL SIX WEEKEND WEATHERMAN...
MARGE, CAN I HAVE A HOT WATER BOTTLE?
MATT GROENING
THIS JUST IN...CHANNEL SIX'S WEATHERMAN WAS FOUND DEAD IN HIS APARTMENT TODAY, A VICTIM OF HYPOTHERMIA.
MARGE! I'M FREEZING IN HERE! HOT WATER BOTTLE!
HOMER, I CAN'T TURN ON THE STOVE. OUR GAS LINE MUST BE FROZEN. PLEASE LET ME TURN UP THE HEAT.
PRETTY EXTREME WAY TO PROVE HOW COLD IT IS. BUT THEN, FRITZ WAS ALWAYS A SHOW OFF.
NO. OUR POWER BILL WAS OUTRAGEOUS LAST MONTH. I THOUGHT IT WAS OUR PHONE BILL.
YOU THOUGHT IT WAS OUR PHONE **NUMBER**.
WE NOW TAKE YOU LIVE TO THE SPRINGFIELD NUCLEAR POWER PLANT FOR A SPECIAL ANNOUNCEMENT.
HELLO. I REGRET TO INFORM YOU THAT SPRINGFIELD WILL BE EXPERIENCING INTERMITTENT POWER OUTAGES UNTIL THIS COLD SNAP ENDS.
I REALIZE THIS WILL MEAN DISCOMFORT FOR SOME AND THE WELCOMING BOSOM OF DEATH FOR OTHERS.
I CAN'T STOP MY TEETH FROM CHATTERING. I EVEN PUT THEM IN A GLASS OF HOT WATER.
PATRIC M. VERRONE SCRIPT
DAN DAVIS PENCILS
MIKE ROTE INKS
NATHAN HAMILL COLORS
KAREN BATES LETTERS
BILL MORRISON EDITOR

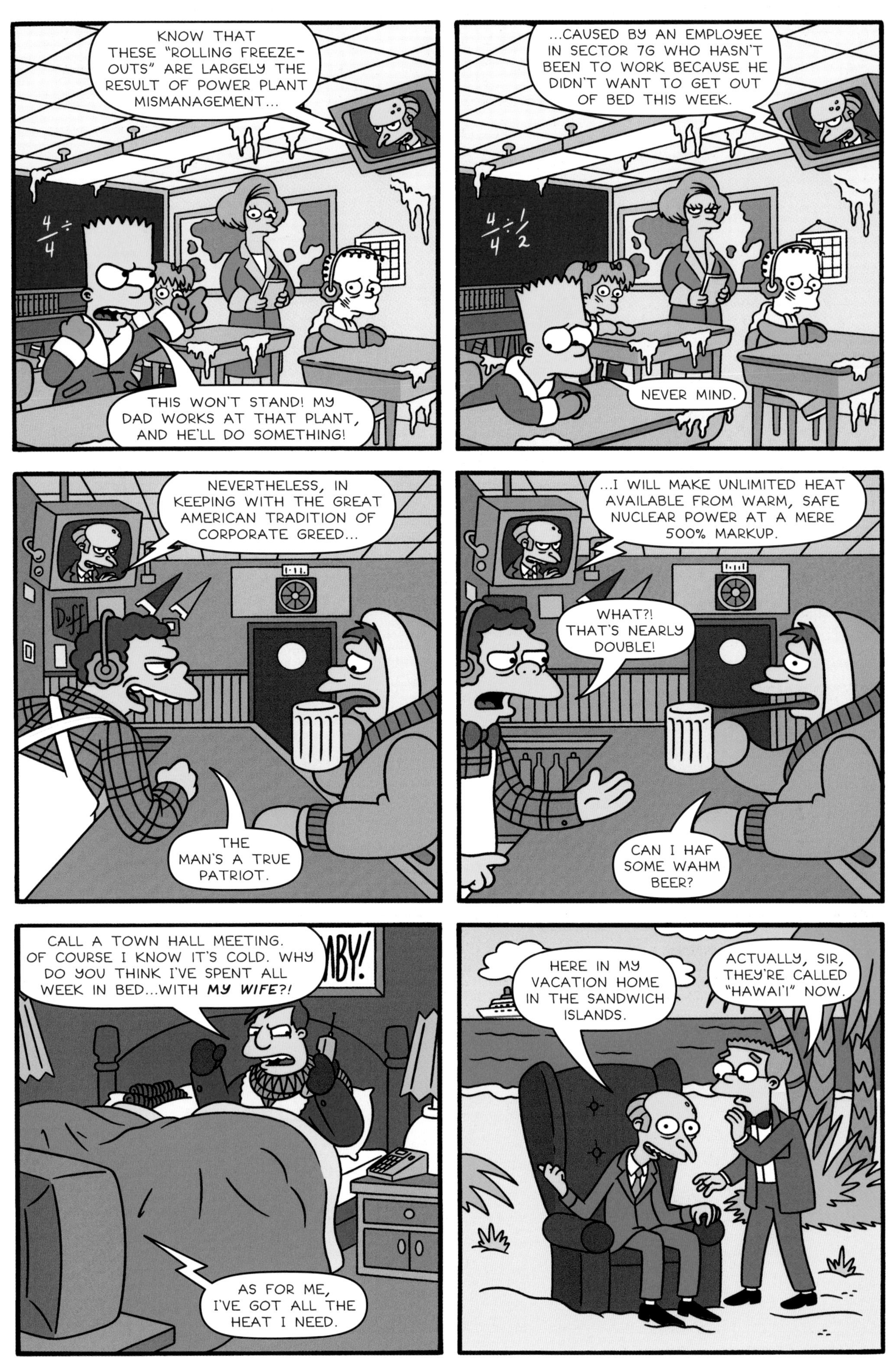
KNOW THAT THESE "ROLLING FREEZE-OUTS" ARE LARGELY THE RESULT OF POWER PLANT MISMANAGEMENT...
4/4 ÷
THIS WON'T STAND! MY DAD WORKS AT THAT PLANT, AND HE'LL DO SOMETHING!
...CAUSED BY AN EMPLOYEE IN SECTOR 7G WHO HASN'T BEEN TO WORK BECAUSE HE DIDN'T WANT TO GET OUT OF BED THIS WEEK.
4/4 ÷ 1/2
NEVER MIND.
NEVERTHELESS, IN KEEPING WITH THE GREAT AMERICAN TRADITION OF CORPORATE GREED...
Duff
THE MAN'S A TRUE PATRIOT.
...I WILL MAKE UNLIMITED HEAT AVAILABLE FROM WARM, SAFE NUCLEAR POWER AT A MERE 500% MARKUP.
WHAT?! THAT'S NEARLY DOUBLE!
CAN I HAF SOME WAHM BEER?
CALL A TOWN HALL MEETING. OF COURSE I KNOW IT'S COLD. WHY DO YOU THINK I'VE SPENT ALL WEEK IN BED...WITH ***MY WIFE?!***
AS FOR ME, I'VE GOT ALL THE HEAT I NEED.
HERE IN MY VACATION HOME IN THE SANDWICH ISLANDS.
ACTUALLY, SIR, THEY'RE CALLED "HAWAI'I" NOW.

IT WAS SO COLD, MY LAWYER HAD HIS HANDS IN **HIS OWN** POCKETS!!
THANK YOU, KRISPY THE CLOWN, FOR THAT NOBLE ATTEMPT AT A "WARM-UP" ACT.
IT'S "KRUSTY," AND YOU SHOULD KNOW SOMETHING ABOUT HOT AIR.
SO...ER...AH... WHAT SHOULD WE DO ABOUT MR. BURNS?
LIGHT HIM ON FIRE.
WARM OURSELVES ON HIS FUNERAL PYRE!
PEOPLE, PEOPLE... IN A MOMENT OF CRISIS WE MUST TURN TO THE BIBLE, MARK, CHAPTER 15, VERSE 13.
HE'S RIGHT. "CRUCIFY HIM!"
IF THERE'S ONE THING WE CAN COUNT ON IN THIS TOWN, IT'S AN ANGRY MOB.
TO THE POWER PLANT!

WE WANT POWER!
WE WANT POWER!
I THINK YOU'D BETTER SPEAK TO THEM, SIR.
I WAS DRAGGED BACK FROM VACATION IN STOCKS FOR *THIS*?
MR. BURNS, WE UNDERSTAND YOUR NEED TO GOUGE AND OVERCHARGE, BUT THINK OF THE CHILDREN AND THE ELDERLY.
WELL, I DO HAVE A SOFT SPOT IN MY HEART FOR THE ELDERLY.
SO YOU'LL MAKE AFFORDABLE POWER AVAILABLE TO THEM AND ANYONE ELSE WHO CAN STAND TO BE IN THE SAME ROOM WITH THEM?
NO, I'LL JUST HAVE THAT SOFT SPOT LOOKED AT BY MY FAVORITE SURGEON IN MARTINIQUE.
TO HADES WITH YE!
AND TAKE US WITH YOU!

THUNK!
UH-OH.
FWASH!
NICE JOB, HOMER. IT'S WARM AGAIN.
YEAH, THANKS, HOMER. I DIDN'T KNOW NUCLEAR POWER COULD BE SO HELPFUL.
A WEEK LATER...
YEAR-ROUND SUMMER IS WONDERFUL, ISN'T IT.
THERE ARE SOME AFTER EFFECTS THAT WILL TAKE SOME GETTING USED TO.
IT'S WORTH IT. YUMPH.
THE END

ERIC ROGERS SCRIPT | PHIL ORTIZ PENCILS | MIKE DECARLO INKS | ROBERT STANLEY COLORS | KAREN BATES LETTERS | BILL MORRISON EDITOR

SNFFFFF!
MMM, THE SWEET SMELL OF ILLEGALLY GOTTEN GAINS!
REEEOOO-REEEOOO!
REEEOOO-REEEOOO!
OH, CHEESE AND CRACKERS... *THE FUZZ!*
ALLEGED PERPETRATOR, PULL OVER, OR I WILL BE FORCED TO SHOOT!
UM, CHIEF, HOW DO WE KNOW FOR SURE THAT'S THE GUY WE'RE SUPPOSED TO BE CHASING?
LOU, YOU KNOW I'M A SHOOT-FIRST, LAWSUIT-LATER COP! NOW, HOLD 'ER STEADY!
WHOA, TOTALLY NOT FEELING AWESOME ANYMORE. AHH... AHH... AHH...
...*CHOO!*
GRODY!

UH-OH... SO NOT COOL!

KUH-PLUMPH!

A MOMENT LATER...
CITIZEN, COME OUT WITH YOUR MITTENS UP!

LOOKS LIKE HE GOT AWAY, LOU!

GOT SOME TRACKS IN THE SNOW, CHIEF. WE SHOULD FOLLOW THEM!
NOT SO FAST. THE PERP LEFT BEHIND SOME DNA TO COLLECT!

UHH...DOESN'T IT JUST MAKE MORE SENSE TO GO AFTER HIM?
IN THIS WEATHER? BRRRR!
INSTEAD, LET'S TAKE THIS UNIDENTIFIED BODY FLUID TO OUR LAB, WHICH WILL TAKE WEEKS TO ANALYZE IT, AND MAY OR MAY NOT I.D. WHO THIS SCUZZ-BUCKET TRULY IS!

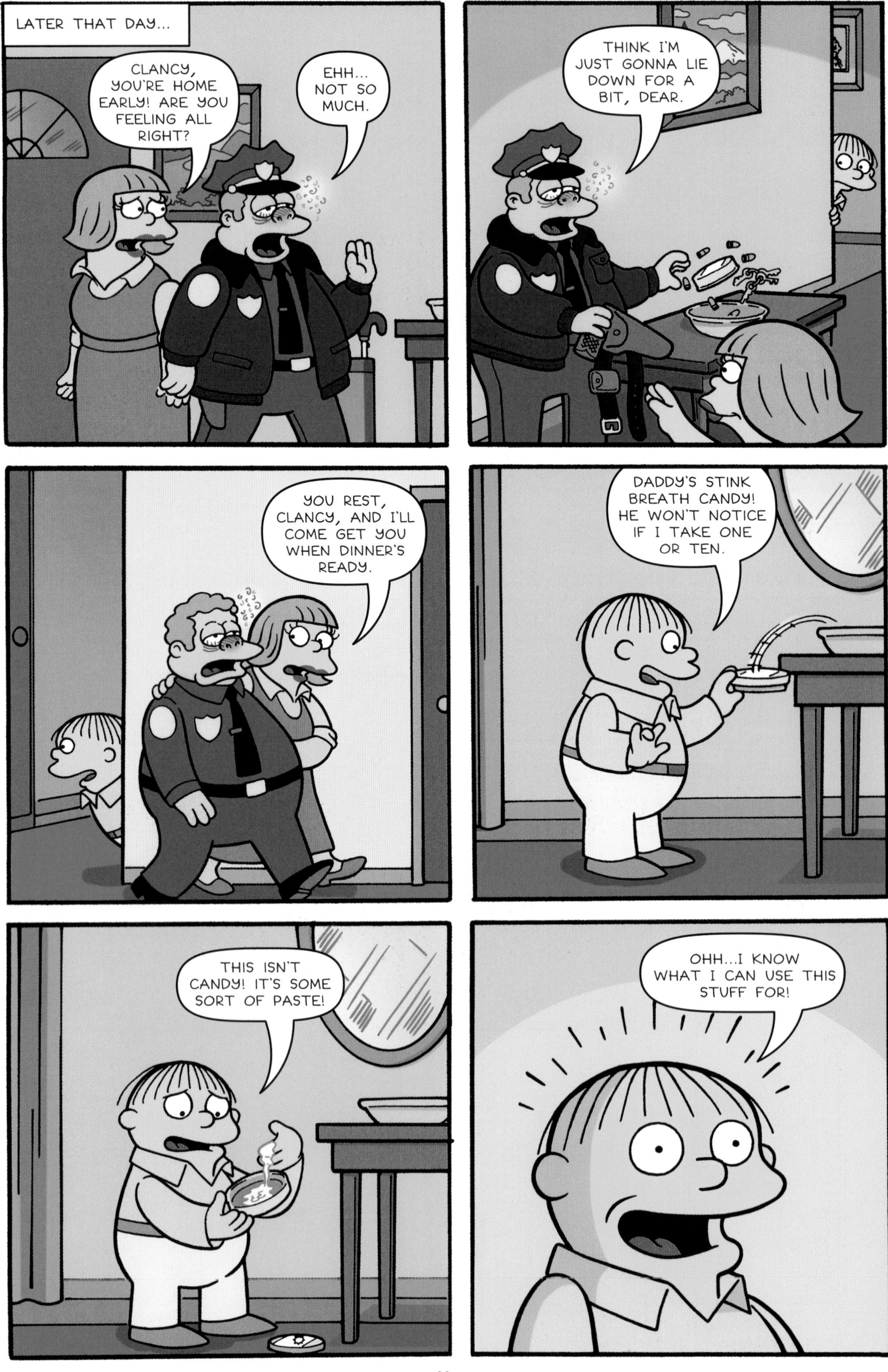
LATER THAT DAY...
CLANCY, YOU'RE HOME EARLY! ARE YOU FEELING ALL RIGHT?
EHH... NOT SO MUCH.
THINK I'M JUST GONNA LIE DOWN FOR A BIT, DEAR.
YOU REST, CLANCY, AND I'LL COME GET YOU WHEN DINNER'S READY.
DADDY'S STINK BREATH CANDY! HE WON'T NOTICE IF I TAKE ONE OR TEN.
THIS ISN'T CANDY! IT'S SOME SORT OF PASTE!
OHH...I KNOW WHAT I CAN USE THIS STUFF FOR!

THAT EVENING...
ARE YOU SURE THIS STUFF IS PASTE, RALPH?
IT FEELS... DIFFERENT.
ONLY ONE WAY TO KNOW FOR SURE...
IT DOESN'T TASTE LIKE PASTE, BUT MAYBE IT'S THE KIND POLICEY MEN USE TO MAKE THEIR HANDCUFFS STICK?
TWENTY-EIGHT OTHER KIDS IN CLASS AND I GET PAIRED WITH YOU AS MY PARTNER?
"TOP OF THE WORLD, MA..."
FEST
GO WASH YOUR FACE, RALPH!
HEY, BOY, I BET YOU CAN HELP ME GET THIS STUFF OFF!
HEE-HEE-HEE!
DING DONG!
AWW...

THERE'S MY FAVORITE GIRL! GIVE US A HUG ALREADY...
ALL RIGHT, ALL RIGHT...I LOVE YOU TOO, YOU SILLY MUTT!
THANKS FOR BABY-SITTING MAGGIE FOR US, MOE. I THINK SHE'S MORE EXCITED ABOUT OUR DATE NIGHT THAN WE ARE!
NO WORRIES, MIDGE. WE'RE GONNA HAVE A GREAT TIME WATCHING THAT "REAL MIDWIVES OF AMISH COUNTRY" MARATHON ON BRAVO!
C'MON, MARGE, MY BELLY IS SO EMPTY, IT'S USING CURSE WORDS!
WE'LL BE BACK BEFORE ELEVEN. YOU HAVE MY CELL NUMBER IF YOU NEED IT. HAVE FUN!
GOOD NIGHT, SWEETIE. MOMMY WILL SEE YOU IN THE MORNING!
SMACK!
THE FOLLOWING MORNING...
MOM? DAD...? LISA?! WHERE THE HECK IS EVERYBODY??
AYE, CARUMBA!

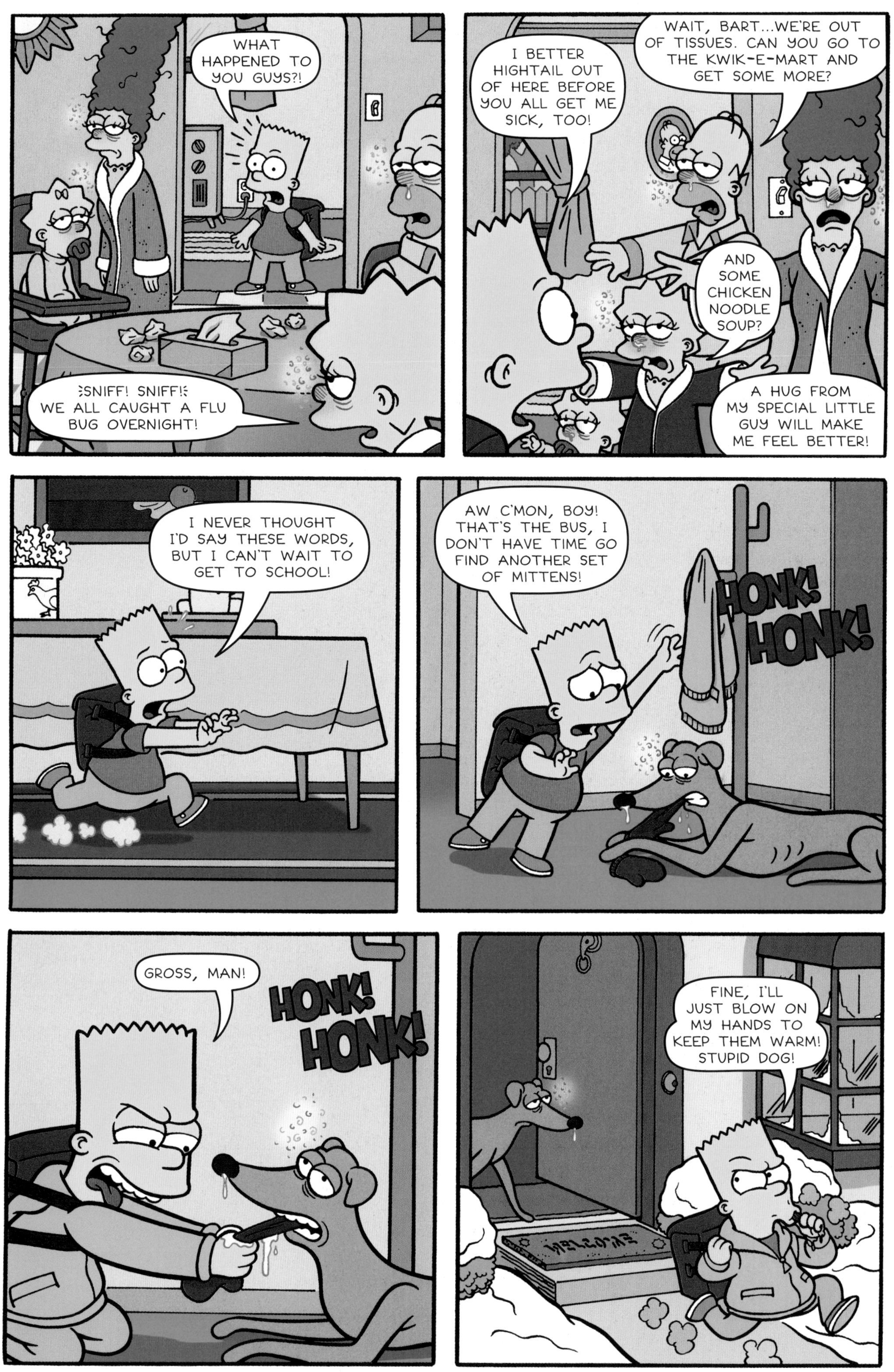
WHAT HAPPENED TO YOU GUYS?!
⁝SNIFF! SNIFF!⁝ WE ALL CAUGHT A FLU BUG OVERNIGHT!
I BETTER HIGHTAIL OUT OF HERE BEFORE YOU ALL GET ME SICK, TOO!
WAIT, BART...WE'RE OUT OF TISSUES. CAN YOU GO TO THE KWIK-E-MART AND GET SOME MORE?
AND SOME CHICKEN NOODLE SOUP?
A HUG FROM MY SPECIAL LITTLE GUY WILL MAKE ME FEEL BETTER!
I NEVER THOUGHT I'D SAY THESE WORDS, BUT I CAN'T WAIT TO GET TO SCHOOL!
AW C'MON, BOY! THAT'S THE BUS, I DON'T HAVE TIME GO FIND ANOTHER SET OF MITTENS!
HONK! HONK!
GROSS, MAN!
HONK! HONK!
FINE, I'LL JUST BLOW ON MY HANDS TO KEEP THEM WARM! STUPID DOG!

LATER, AT SCHOOL...
MIL-HEEZY! WHAT'S THE HAPS?
UHH...I HAVE NO IDEA WHAT YOU SAID, BUT IT SOUNDED COOL!
LATER ON...
THAT'S THE SIXTH PIECE OF FRUIT YOU'VE MANHANDLED! JUST TAKE ONE AND MOVE ON!
B-BUT THEY ALL LOOK SO DELICIOUS. I CAN'T MAKE UP MY MIND!
I'LL TAKE THAT APPLE...
KEEP THE LINE MOVING, MILHOUSE.
KRRUNCH!
AFTER LUNCH...
TEACHER'S LOUNGE
A BIT AFTER THAT...
KOFF! KOFF! OKAY, STUDENTS, I'VE GRADED YOUR POP QUIZZES FROM YESTERDAY...
UHH...MISS KRABAPPEL? I DON'T FEEL SO GOOD.
AFTER WHAT YOU SCORED ON THE QUIZ, NEITHER WOULD I, BART.

THE END OF THE SCHOOL DAY!
SPRINGFIELD ELEMENTARY SCHOOL
BRRRRRINNNG!
AND OVER THE NEXT FEW HOURS...

RE-ELECT QUIMBY... OR THE TERRORISTS WIN!

THE NEXT MORNING...
DR. HIBBERT, THANK GOD YOU'RE HERE! WE HAVE AN EMERGENCY!
AH HEE HEE HEE...WHAT IS IT??
FOLLOW ME!

I THINK THE ENTIRE CITY HAS COME DOWN WITH THE FLU!
SPORT!
GOLF

KOFF! KOFF! KENT BROCKMAN LIVE WITH BREAKING NEWS FROM THE MOST POPULAR PLACE IN TOWN THIS MORNING...THE DOCTOR'S OFFICE!
IN A RELATED STORY, I HAVE A FEVER OF 107 AND WOKE UP IN A POOL OF MY OWN SWEAT!
CO-PAY DUE AT VISIT
MAYOR
KB
FLU FIGHTERS
MY GOODNESS, EVERY ONE OF MY PATIENTS MUST HAVE CAUGHT THIS BUG!
ALMOST. THERE'S ONE PERSON WHO CANCELLED HIS APPOINTMENT THIS MORNING TO LEAVE TOWN BEFORE HE CAUGHT THE FLU, TOO!

I DROVE ALL THE WAY HERE TO ENSURE I DIDN'T HAVE TO BREATHE ANY MORE OF THAT FLU-INFESTED SPRINGFIELD AIR!
WELCOME TO SHELBYVILLE INTERNATIONAL AIRPORT
OUR CURRENT THREAT LEVEL IS 'OH NO YOU DI'N'T!'

THE SOONER I'M IN THE SKY, THE BETTER!
HAVE A WONDERFUL FLIGHT, SIR.

A MOMENT LATER...
23A... 23A...?
YOU FOUND IT, FRIEND...

...RIGHT NEXT TO ME.

A PLEASURE TO MEET YOU. I'LL TRY TO REFRAIN FROM RECITING DIALOGUE FROM THE "DOCTOR WHO" EPISODES I'LL BE WATCHING DURING OUR FLIGHT!
NO WORRIES. I'LL BE ZONKED OUT ON MY FLU MEDS BEFORE WE EVEN TAKE OFF.

LADIES AND GENTLEMEN, THE PLANE DOORS ARE NOW CLOSED, AND WE'LL BE IN THE AIR IN JUST A FEW MOMENTS...
WORST... IRONIC ENDING... EVER.
THE END

THE SIMPSON FAMILY CHRISTMAS CARDS
HRMMM...JUST ONCE I WISH I COULD GET A DECENT FAMILY CHRISTMAS PICTURE.
MATT GROENING
TONY DIGEROLAMO SCRIPT
JOHN DELANEY PENCILS
HOWARD SHUM INKS
ART VILLANUEVA COLORS
KAREN BATES LETTERS
BILL MORRISON EDITOR
"OH, MY."
"POOR BART."
"OH, DEAR."
DUFF
"POOR HOMIE."

"NEVER AGAIN."
"AT LEAST HE WAS POLITE."
"POOR LENNY."
LISTEN, YOU FOUR, I DON'T CARE HOW IT HAPPENS, BUT YOU **WILL** GIVE ME A NICE PICTURE THIS YEAR!
AND MAKE SURE YOU WEAR YOUR BEST CLOTHES!
AWWW...
AND THE PICTURE BETTER BE ***NICE!***
MERRY CHRISTMAS
THE END

GETTING THERE IS HALF THE BATTLE
PATRIC M. VERRONE SCRIPT
NATHAN HAMILL COLORS
NINA MATSUMOTO PENCILS
KAREN BATES LETTERS
MIKE ROTE INKS
BILL MORRISON EDITOR
THIS BOTTLE CAP ENTITLES THE BEARER TO AN ALL EXPENSE PAID WEEKEND VACATION FOR A FAMILY OF FIVE AT THE DUFF SKI RESORT IN DUFFSPEN, COLORADO.
ALWAYS DRINK RESPONSIBLY (MEANING DON'T BLAME US IF YOU GET HAMMERED AND SKI INTO A PINE TREE).
WOW, HOMER, HOW DID YOU EVER READ WHAT IT SAID?
I PASSED OUT ON THE CAP AT MOE'S AND THE WRITING SEARED INTO MY CORNEA.
MATT GROENING
SO I WAS THINKING OF MAKING THE TRIP THIS WEEKEND.
OH, HOMIE, THAT'S WONDERFUL. KIDS! WE'RE GOING SKIING!
BUT, MARGE, I WAS PLANNING TO BRING MOE, BARNEY, LENNY, AND CARL.
WHEN YOU SEE YOUR CHILDREN IN THEIR NEW SNOW GEAR, YOU'LL DEFINITELY WANT TO TAKE THEM.
TAKE US WITH YOU OR ELSE.
DEFINITELY.

CAPITAL CITY AIR SPRINGFIEL
WELL, THIS IS THE BUSIEST TRAVEL WEEKEND OF THE YEAR, AND THERE'S A MAJOR STORM HEADING THIS WAY, AND OUR AIRLINE JUST DECLARED BANKRUPTCY.
ARE YOU SURE YOU WANT TO TRAVEL TO DUFFSPEN TODAY?
DEFINITELY.
ARRIVALS
WELL, WE HAVE A FLIGHT WITH CONNECTIONS IN BROCKWAY, OGDENVILLE, AND NORTH HAVERBROOK.
WE'LL TAKE IT.
LATER...
MOM, WE'VE BEEN SITTING AT THE GATE FOR HOURS. WHEN ARE WE GETTING ON THE PLANE?
PATIENCE, HONEY.
LATER STILL...
MOM, WE'VE BEEN SITTING ON THE TARMAC FOR HOURS. WHEN ARE WE GOING TO TAKEOFF?
PATIENCE, HONEY.
ISSUE 104
IN FLIGHT
EVEN LATER STILL...
WE'VE BEEN CIRCLING BROCKWAY FOR HOURS...
I KNOW, I KNOW!! WHEN ARE WE GOING TO LAND?!
PATIENCE, HONEY.

YOU MISSED YOUR CONNECTION TO OGDENVILLE. THE NEXT FLIGHT ISN'T UNTIL MORNING, BUT WE CAN PUT YOU UP OVERNIGHT AT BROCKWAY'S FINEST ADDRESS.
A FANCY RESORT HOTEL?
DELAYED
22
AIR
BROCKWAY
WELCOME TO BROCKWAY WATCH YOUR VALUABLES
SIZE LIMIT
NO, TERMINAL 2.
TERMINAL 2
ARE THERE ANY FLIGHTS TO DUFFSPEN?
ZZZZ...
ZZZ...
YOU'RE IN LUCK. THERE ARE FIVE OPEN SEATS ON A FLIGHT LEAVING IN TEN MINUTES, AND IT ONLY HAS ONE STOP... IN SPRINGFIELD.
WE'LL TAKE IT.
BACK IN SPRINGFIELD...
SAN DIEGO
ORLANDO
ST. LOUIS
DELAYED
CAN WE MAKE THE CONNECTION TO THE FLIGHT TO DUFFSPEN?
EASILY...
SPRINGFIELD
...BECAUSE IT'S NOT LEAVING UNTIL TOMORROW...
...BECAUSE THE PILOT DIDN'T SHOW UP.
YOU'RE SUPPOSED TO BE SAD.
NOT SO, MY GOOD MAN...
BECAUSE I **AM** THAT PILOT!
OH LORD.

HOMER, ARE YOU SURE YOU KNOW WHAT YOU'RE DOING?
CLOSE. I'M SURE I **DON'T** KNOW WHAT I'M DOING. BUT REMEMBER, I'M A TRAINED ASTRONAUT.
OF COURSE, THIS ISN'T A PROBLEM WHEN YOU'RE IN SPACE.
HOMER, MAYBE WE SHOULD TAKE A TRAIN
THIS IS NOT WHAT I MEANT, HOMER.
NO TIME TO COMPLAIN. WE'RE ABOUT TO HEAD INTO A TUNNEL.
EXCUSE ME, CONDUCTOR, DOES THIS TRAIN GO TO DUFFSPEN?
YOU'RE IN LUCK. IT GOES WHEREVER YOU WANT IT TO GO! THIS IS THE POLAR EXPRESS!
HOLD ON. I SKIMMED THAT BOOK AND SPED THROUGH THAT MOVIE ON DVD. THE POLAR EXPRESS WAS JUST A DREAM.
THEN I GUESS YOU'RE OUT OF LUCK!
CONDUCTOR
NICE WORK, BART. THAT WAS OUR TICKET TO RIDE.
HE TOLD **ME** IT WAS THE UNDER-GROUND RAILROAD.
LOOK, I'LL GET YOU THERE SOMEHOW.

LATER...
WHO KNEW "CHANGE" INCLUDED SELLING RIDES ON MARINE ONE?
GOTTA PAY DOWN THAT DEFICIT SOMEHOW.
HOMER, THIS IS THE MOST RIDICULOUS THING YET.
I SAID "YET."
WELCOME TO DUFFSPEN, MR. SIMPSON. THE REST OF YOUR PARTY HAS BEEN WAITING FOR YOU.
THE REST OF MY WHO HAVE BEEN WHAT NOW?
WE'LL HAVE OUR COURTESY TRAM TAKE YOUR FAMILY TO THEIR ACCOMMODATIONS DIRECTLY.
THAT SOUNDS GREAT.
SOON...
HEY! THESE ARE OUR "ACCOMMODATIONS?!"
BART, CAN YOU TEACH ME TO USE THAT CROSSBOW?
DEFINITELY.
THE END

STORY: GRAFF/MCCANN **ART**: GONZALEZ LOYO/HARKIN/BATES

ERIC ROGERS SCRIPT | MIKE KAZALEH PENCILS | MIKE ROTE INKS | NATHAN HAMILL COLORS | KAREN BATES LETTERS | BILL MORRISON EDITOR

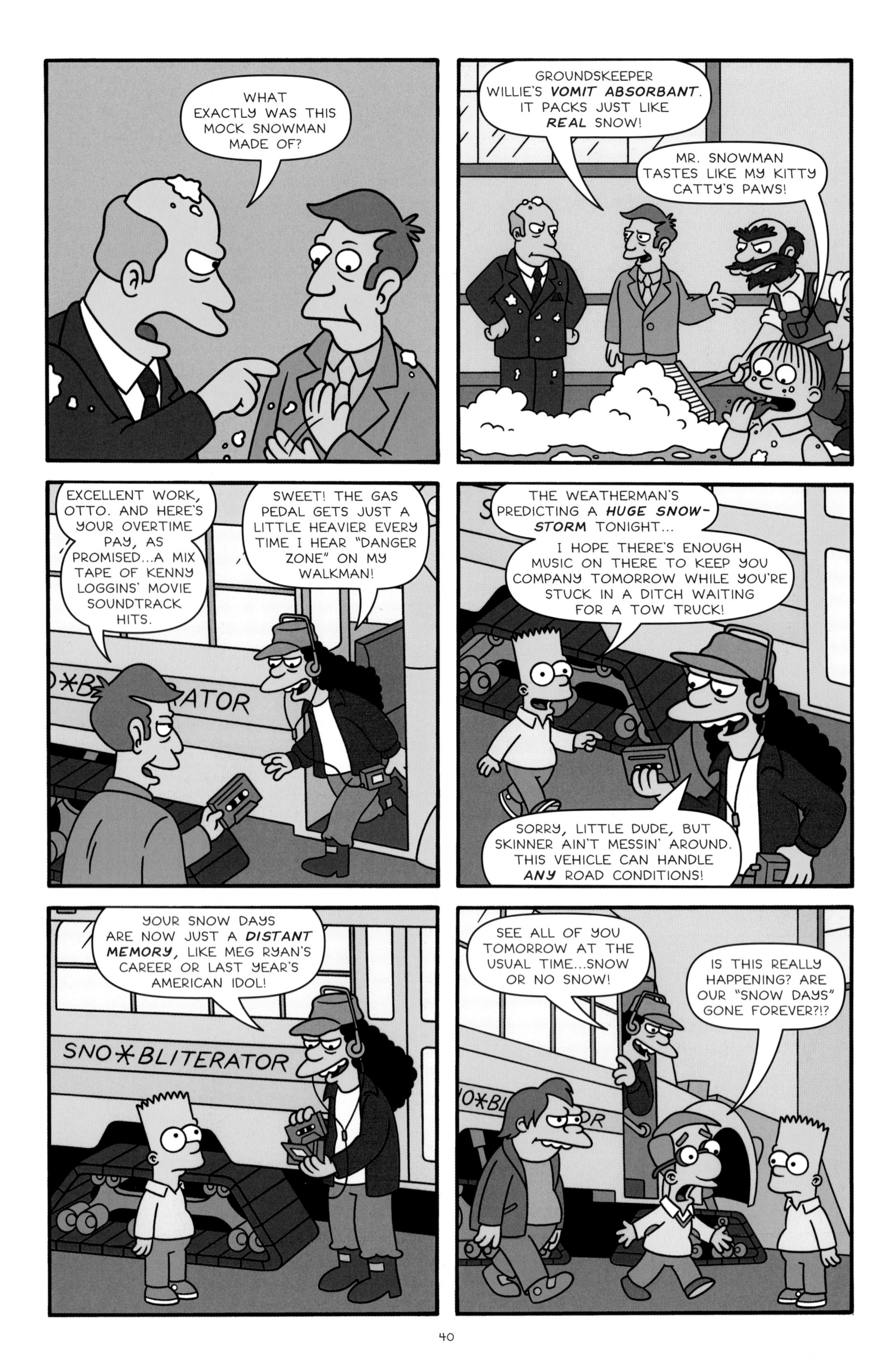
WHAT EXACTLY WAS THIS MOCK SNOWMAN MADE OF?
GROUNDSKEEPER WILLIE'S VOMIT ABSORBANT. IT PACKS JUST LIKE REAL SNOW!
MR. SNOWMAN TASTES LIKE MY KITTY CATTY'S PAWS!
EXCELLENT WORK, OTTO. AND HERE'S YOUR OVERTIME PAY, AS PROMISED...A MIX TAPE OF KENNY LOGGINS' MOVIE SOUNDTRACK HITS.
SWEET! THE GAS PEDAL GETS JUST A LITTLE HEAVIER EVERY TIME I HEAR "DANGER ZONE" ON MY WALKMAN!
THE WEATHERMAN'S PREDICTING A HUGE SNOW-STORM TONIGHT...
I HOPE THERE'S ENOUGH MUSIC ON THERE TO KEEP YOU COMPANY TOMORROW WHILE YOU'RE STUCK IN A DITCH WAITING FOR A TOW TRUCK!
SORRY, LITTLE DUDE, BUT SKINNER AIN'T MESSIN' AROUND. THIS VEHICLE CAN HANDLE ANY ROAD CONDITIONS!
YOUR SNOW DAYS ARE NOW JUST A DISTANT MEMORY, LIKE MEG RYAN'S CAREER OR LAST YEAR'S AMERICAN IDOL!
SNO✱BLITERATOR
SEE ALL OF YOU TOMORROW AT THE USUAL TIME...SNOW OR NO SNOW!
IS THIS REALLY HAPPENING? ARE OUR "SNOW DAYS" GONE FOREVER?!?

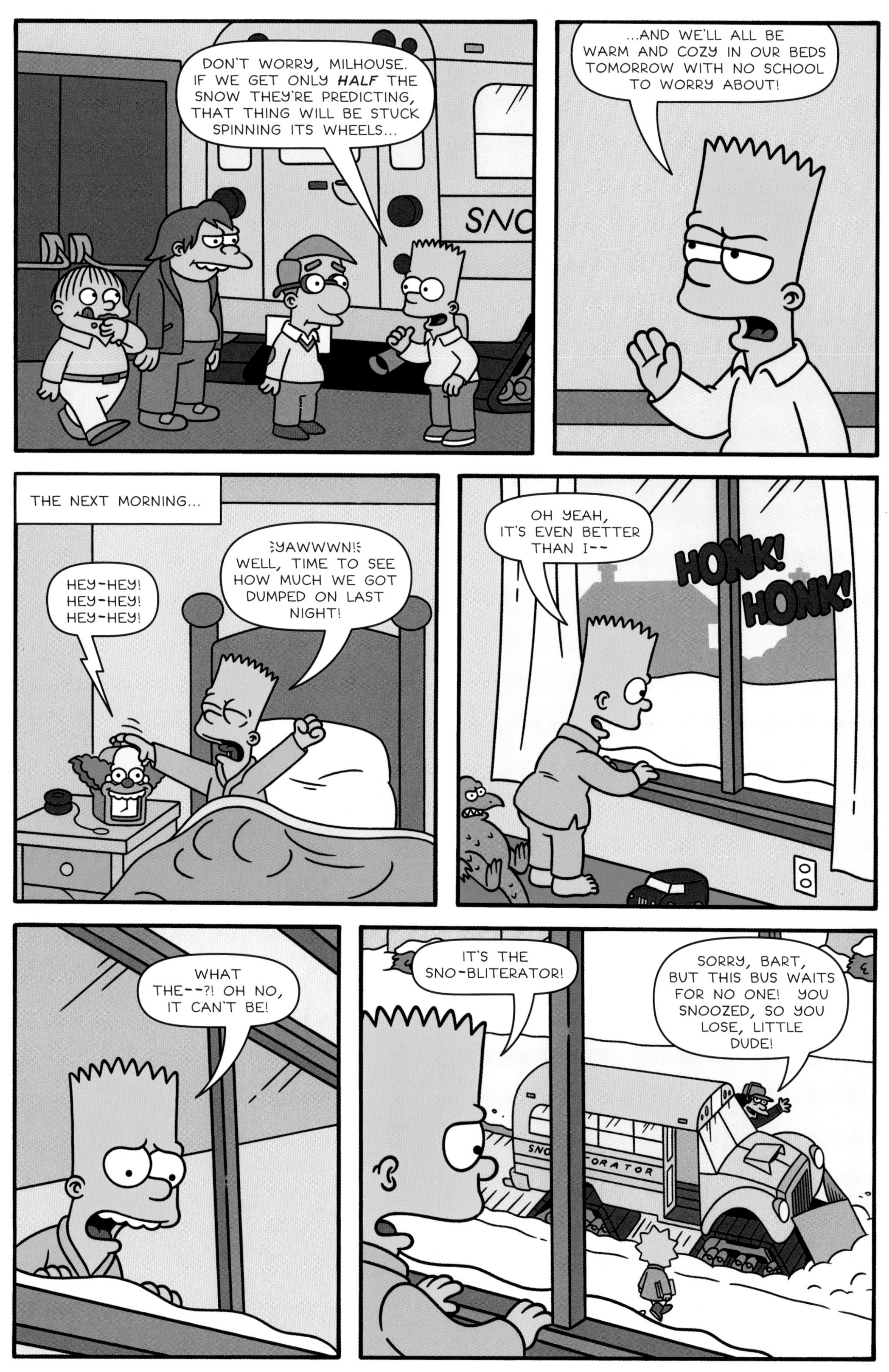
DON'T WORRY, MILHOUSE. IF WE GET ONLY HALF THE SNOW THEY'RE PREDICTING, THAT THING WILL BE STUCK SPINNING ITS WHEELS...
SNO
...AND WE'LL ALL BE WARM AND COZY IN OUR BEDS TOMORROW WITH NO SCHOOL TO WORRY ABOUT!
THE NEXT MORNING...
HEY-HEY! HEY-HEY! HEY-HEY!
:YAWWWN!: WELL, TIME TO SEE HOW MUCH WE GOT DUMPED ON LAST NIGHT!
OH YEAH, IT'S EVEN BETTER THAN I--
HONK! HONK!
WHAT THE--?! OH NO, IT CAN'T BE!
IT'S THE SNO-BLITERATOR!
SORRY, BART, BUT THIS BUS WAITS FOR NO ONE! YOU SNOOZED, SO YOU LOSE, LITTLE DUDE!

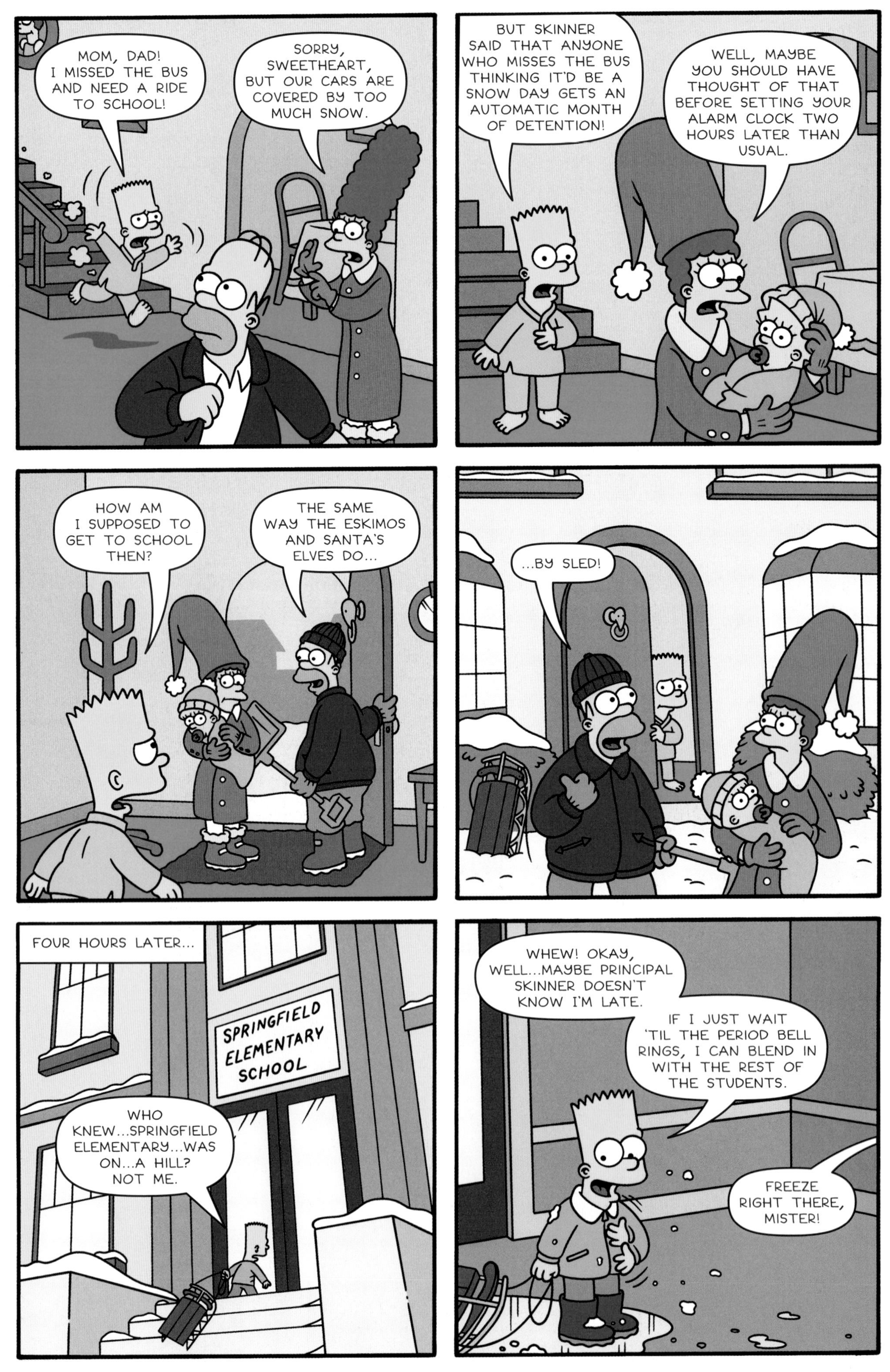
MOM, DAD! I MISSED THE BUS AND NEED A RIDE TO SCHOOL!
SORRY, SWEETHEART, BUT OUR CARS ARE COVERED BY TOO MUCH SNOW.
BUT SKINNER SAID THAT ANYONE WHO MISSES THE BUS THINKING IT'D BE A SNOW DAY GETS AN AUTOMATIC MONTH OF DETENTION!
WELL, MAYBE YOU SHOULD HAVE THOUGHT OF THAT BEFORE SETTING YOUR ALARM CLOCK TWO HOURS LATER THAN USUAL.
HOW AM I SUPPOSED TO GET TO SCHOOL THEN?
THE SAME WAY THE ESKIMOS AND SANTA'S ELVES DO...
...BY SLED!
FOUR HOURS LATER...
SPRINGFIELD ELEMENTARY SCHOOL
WHO KNEW...SPRINGFIELD ELEMENTARY...WAS ON...A HILL? NOT ME.
WHEW! OKAY, WELL...MAYBE PRINCIPAL SKINNER DOESN'T KNOW I'M LATE.
IF I JUST WAIT 'TIL THE PERIOD BELL RINGS, I CAN BLEND IN WITH THE REST OF THE STUDENTS.
FREEZE RIGHT THERE, MISTER!

YER NOT TRACKING FRESH SNOW INTO MY HALLWAYS, BART SIMPSON!
NOW YE EITHER SWEEP UP THIS MESS AND I'LL KEEP YER TARDINESS A SECRET, OR I GO TELL SKINNER MESELF!
BRRING-ING!
YES! SAVED BY THE BELL!
SORRY, WILLIE, BUT I'M JUST ANOTHER PUNCTUAL STUDENT TRYING TO GET TO MY NEXT CLASS ON TIME!
JUST NEED TO DRY OFF A LITTLE BEFORE GETTING TO CLASS TO BE SAFE AND THEN--
OOF!
NICE OF YOU TO JOIN US FOR THE SECOND HALF OF THE DAY, SIMPSON.
YOU'LL HAVE PLENTY OF TIME TO MAKE UP WHAT YOU MISSED IN DETENTION!

LATER THAT DAY, IN THE DETENTION HALL...
I'VE NEVER SEEN BART LIKE THIS BEFORE. ALL THIS "SNO-BLITERATOR" BUSINESS IS REALLY TICKING HIM OFF!
OH NO, I KNOW THAT LOOK.. IT MEANS THIS TIME, IT'S PERSONAL!
UHH, BART...ARE YOU OKAY?
THERE ARE FEW THINGS WE KIDS CAN LOOK FORWARD TO DURING THE SCHOOL YEAR...
...TERRORIZING SUBSTITUTE TEACHERS, EATING THE CANDY SALE CANDY BEFORE YOU SEL IT, AND SNOW DAYS.
AND NOW SKINNER WANTS TO TAKE ONE OF THOSE INALIENABLE RIGHTS AWAY, JUST BECAUSE HE CAN?!
NO WAY, MAN! WE DESERVE THESE SNOW DAYS, WHETHER SKINNER THINKS SO OR NOT.
BUS STOP
SNO*BLITERATOR
WE'LL BE READY FOR THE NEXT STORM, BUT I'M GONNA NEED HELP TAKING THE SNO-BLITERATOR OUT OF COMMISSION! WHO'S WITH ME?
DESTROYING SCHOOL PROPERTY OFF SCHOOL PROPERTY? DONE!
OHH... PICK ME, PICK ME!
YOU DO REALIZE I'VE OVERHEARD EVERY WORD YOU'RE SAYING...
AW CRUD. ARE YOU GONNA TELL ON US?
NAH. WHATEVER YOU DO, DO IT RIGHT...
...WE TEACHERS LOVE SNOW DAYS EVEN MORE THAN YOU KIDS!

A FEW NIGHTS LATER, BEFORE ANOTHER PREDICTED SNOWFALL...
WELL, THE WEATHER OUT HERE IS FRIGHTFUL, BUT MY WHEELS ARE SO DELIGHTFUL...
SNO*BLITERATOR

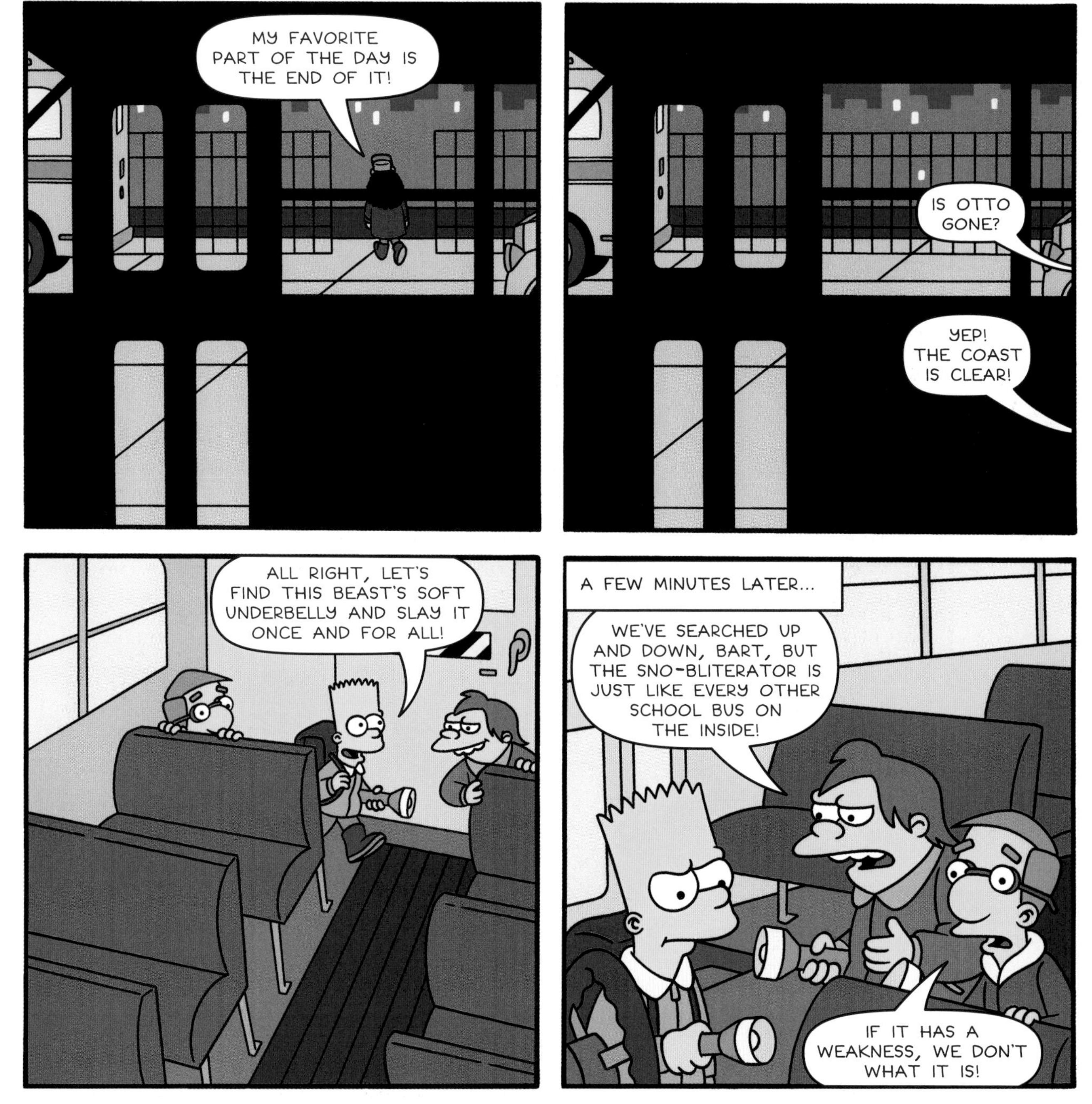
MY FAVORITE PART OF THE DAY IS THE END OF IT!
IS OTTO GONE?
YEP! THE COAST IS CLEAR!
ALL RIGHT, LET'S FIND THIS BEAST'S SOFT UNDERBELLY AND SLAY IT ONCE AND FOR ALL!
A FEW MINUTES LATER...
WE'VE SEARCHED UP AND DOWN, BART, BUT THE SNO-BLITERATOR IS JUST LIKE EVERY OTHER SCHOOL BUS ON THE INSIDE!
IF IT HAS A WEAKNESS, WE DON'T WHAT IT IS!

THAT'S EXACTLY WHY I BROUGHT REINFORCEMENTS FROM HOME!

TRUST ME... THIS GLORIFIED SNOW PLOW MAKES ITS LAST PICK-UP TOMORROW MORNING!
SNO*BLITERATOR

HEH HEH HEH HEH!
GLUG! GLUG! GLUG!
SQUISHEE

THE NEXT MORNING...
YOU LOOK CHIPPER FOR SOMEONE WHO HATES GOING TO SCHOOL...
THAT'S BECAUSE YOU'RE ABOUT TO WITNESS MY GREATEST ACHIEVEMENT YET!
WHOA, BART SIMPSON SMILING AS HE GETS ON THE BUS! NOW I'VE SEEN EVERYTHING!
THAT'S WHAT YOU THINK...
A FEW MINUTES LATER...
I GOT THAT ZOOM-ZOOM-PLOW! CHECK OUT MY ZOOM-ZOOM-PLOW...
UNNHH!!
SPLAT!
WHOA!
GOTTA GET THAT CRUD OFF MY WINDSHIELD SO I CAN SEE...
SPLLLSH!
NOW WHAT'S GOING ON?!

AH...MUCH BETT--
LADY, LOOK OUT!
DUUUUUUUDE!!!
WHUUH...THAT WAS CLOSE, BUT I'VE NEVER FELT MORE ALIVE!
SNO
WHAT'S WRONG WITH MY HANDS?! THEY'RE STUCK TO THE WHEEL!
WHOA, TALK ABOUT WEIRD-A-PALOOZA...
EEEEEEEEE!
AHHHHHHHH!!!
BRRSSSSHHK!

ICE SKATING POND?! OH FOR THE LOVE OF...
THIS IS WORKING TOO WELL! DESTROYING THE SNO-BLITERATOR ISN'T SUPPOSED TO GET US KILLED!
GOTTA DO SOMETHING!
OTTO, IF YOU DON'T PICK UP SPEED RIGHT NOW, THE BUS IS GOING TO CRASH RIGHT THROUGH THE ICE!
NOT ON MY WATCH!
WHUMP!
KEEEE-RRRAAACK!
SPLOOSH!
THE GAS PEDAL IS STUCK! I CAN'T SLOW US DOWN!
THEN THE ONLY WAY TO STOP THIS THING IS TO CRASH INTO SOMETHING SOLID!
EVERYBODY BUCKLE UP FOR AN EMERGENCY LANDING!!

SKINNER, THIS SNO-BLITERATOR IDEA IS SAVING THE SCHOOL A LOT OF MONEY THIS WINTER. I'D LIKE TO REWARD YOUR EFFORTS BY OFFERING YOU THE POSITION OF "ASSISTANT SUPERINTENDENT"!
OH MY. I'M SO HONORED! OF COURSE, MY ANSWER IS--
NOOO!
A FEW MINUTES LATER...
THAT WAS THE MOST SCARED I'VE EVER BEEN IN MY LIFE! I MIGHT NEVER TAKE THE BUS AGAIN!
I'M THINKING VERY SERIOUSLY ABOUT LEGAL ACTION! SOMEONE HAS TO PAY FOR MY YEARS OF INEVITABLE THERAPY!
SKIIINNEERR!!!
YES!
YOUR PET PROJECT JUST COST US EVERYTHING WE SAVED AND THEN SOME!
FORGET THE PROMOTION...YOU'LL BE WORKING OVERTIME TO PAY FOR THIS DAMAGE UNTIL YOU'RE 100!
WELL, SCHOOL'S OUT THE REST OF THE DAY, HUH? GUESS WE ALL KNOW WHAT THAT MEANS...
SNOW DAY!
THE END

HOMER, THE CHILDREN ARE UP WAY PAST THEIR BEDTIME.
DON'T WORRY, MARGE, THEY HAVE ALL YEAR TO CATCH UP ON THEIR SLEEP.
...AND HERE'S HOPING WE ALL MAKE A TRIED AND TRUE EFFORT TO **KEEP** OUR RESOLUTIONS IN THE **NEW YEAR**...
BUT FIRST, LET'S REMEMBER THE RESOLUTIONS THAT WE **COULDN'T** KEEP SO WE CAN AVOID MAKING THE SAME MISTAKES.
BART, WE'LL BEGIN WITH YOUR RESOLUTION TO NEVER MAKE NOISES USING MORE THAN ONE ORIFICE AT A TI--
OOMPH!
HAPPY NEW YEAR AND WELCOME TO PLANET HYPE, THE WORLD'S LARGEST **CELEBRITY-THEMED** CHAIN RESTAURANT. THIS IS THE CLOSEST MOST OF YOU WILL EVER COME TO HOLLYWOOD IN YOUR FLABBY LITTLE LIVES.
PLANET HYPE
OH, IT'S JUST ABOUT **MIDNIGHT**! GET READY FOR THE COUNTDOWN.
NO ONE THROW AWAY ANYTHING HE TOUCHES! BY THE TIME I'M DONE POSTING THIS JUNK ON **EBUY**, THIS DINNER WILL HAVE PAID FOR ITSELF!
IT'S GOING TO BE A HAPPY NEW YEAR INDEED FOR **YOURS TRULY**, IF MY **RESOLUTION KEEPER 3000** WORKS AS PLANNED...
NOW I'LL JUST POSITION MYSELF IN THE MIDDLE OF THE RESTAURANT LIKE SO, THEN MAKE WITH THE TURNING ON OF THE MACHINE AND THE WAITING FOR THE **MAGIC** TO HAPPEN...
CLICK!

ERIC ROGERS SCRIPT | ***JOEY NILGES*** PENCILS | ***KEN WHEATON*** INKS | ***KAREN BATES*** LETTERS | ***ROBERT STANLEY*** COLORS | ***BILL MORRISON*** EDITOR

I KNOW I SAY IT EVERY YEAR, BUT **THIS** TIME I **MEAN IT**! I AM GOING **TO LOSE WEIGHT AND KEEP IT OFF**!
NO MORE! I AM GOING TO STOP DATING THESE HOT, NUBILE BIMBOS AND...ER, AH...**RE-DEDICATE MYSELF** TO MY FAITHFUL WIFE.
BRRRING!
THE WIFE
PERHAPS IF I AM A TAD MORE **FRIENDLY** AND LESS CRITICAL TO ONE AND ALL, I WON'T FIND MYSELF SO VERY ALONE **NEXT** NEW YEAR'S EVE.
YOU KNOW, SWEETIE, I THINK YOU'RE RIGHT ...I WOULD BE A **MUCH** BETTER DOCTOR IF I ACTUALLY WENT TO A **LEGITIMATE** MEDICAL SCHOOL. I'M GOING TO **ENROLL** FIRST THING TOMORROW!
EERRAAAHBLABBABABA GRRAWW...CATS!
I COULDN'T AGREE MORE... PERHAPS WE ALL SHOULD **GIVE MORE**. I'M GOING TO TRY AND BE JUST LIKE YOU THIS YEAR, AND I'LL START BY **PAYING OFF MY TAB** AT MOE'S.
NOW I SHALL TRACK MY NEW LITTLE GUINEA PIGS OVER THE COURSE OF THE YEAR **HEY LADY!** AND DOCUMENT MY FINDINGS, WHICH WILL UNDOUBTEDLY LEAD TO MY WINNING OF THE **NOBEL PRIZE**!

THE NEXT DAY...
HOMIE, YOU'RE GOING TO NEED THIS IF YOU'RE GOING TO SHOVEL SNOW OFF THE DRIVEWAY, AREN'T YOU?
NO TIME, MARGE! I'M GOING OUT FOR A RUN. EVERYTHING ELSE CAN WAIT UNTIL I START TO SHED THESE EXCESS POUNDS!
GO, HOME-BOY!
ALL RIGHT, DAD!
JOE! WHAT'S ALL THIS ABOUT?
BREAKFAST IN BED, HONEY. I'VE DECIDED THAT I'M GOING TO BE A BETTER...ER, AH... HUSBAND TO YOU THIS YEAR, STARTING NOW!
HARK, FAIR MAIDEN! LET ME SHIELD YOU FROM WINTER'S SLUSHY KISS WITH MY AUTHENTIC "FALL GUY" LEATHER JACKET!
THE FALL GUY
SEASON 3
83 - 84
OH MY, WHAT A GENTLE-MAN!
SO IS IT VERY HARD TO GET INTO THIS MEDICAL SCHOOL?
DO YOU LIKE DISSECTING LIVING THINGS AND SAYING THE WORD "STAT?"
WHO DOESN'T?
THEN YOU'RE IN!
SMC
SPRINGFIELD MEDICAL COLLEGE
ADMITTED
HAPPY NEW YEAR, MOE. HERE'S FIVE DOLLARS TO GO TOWARDS PAYING OFF MY TAB.
HA HA HA! GOOD ONE, BARN. HERE, FIRST DRINK OF THE YEAR'S ON ME!
NO WAY! I WON'T TAKE ANOTHER DRINK FROM YOU UNLESS I'VE PAID FOR IT, AND I CAN'T DO THAT UNTIL I'VE PAID OFF MY ENTIRE TAB! SO GOOD DAY TO YOU, SIR!

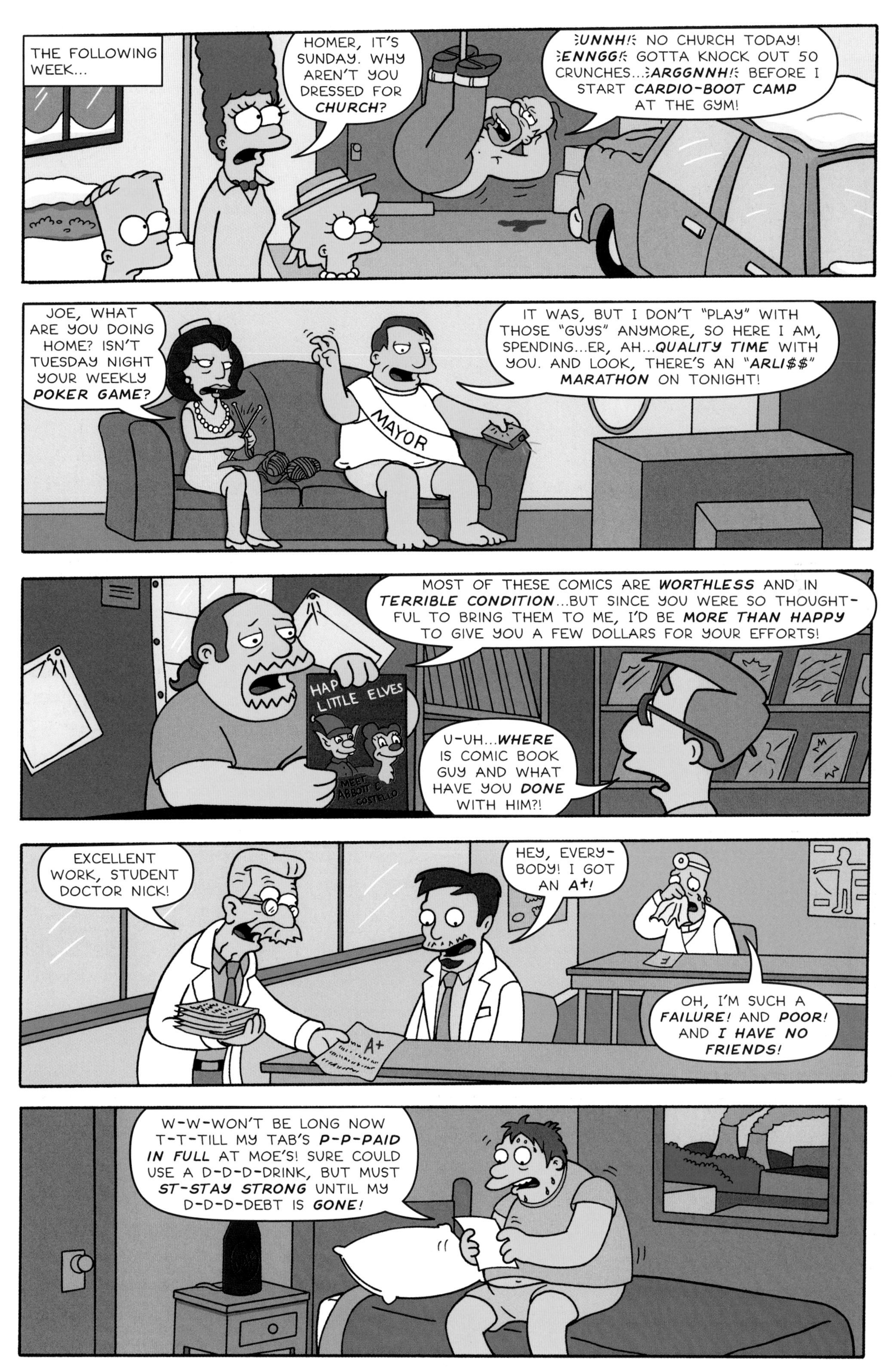
THE FOLLOWING WEEK...
HOMER, IT'S SUNDAY. WHY AREN'T YOU DRESSED FOR CHURCH?
UNNH! NO CHURCH TODAY! ENNGG! GOTTA KNOCK OUT 50 CRUNCHES... ARGGNNH! BEFORE I START CARDIO-BOOT CAMP AT THE GYM!
JOE, WHAT ARE YOU DOING HOME? ISN'T TUESDAY NIGHT YOUR WEEKLY POKER GAME?
IT WAS, BUT I DON'T "PLAY" WITH THOSE "GUYS" ANYMORE, SO HERE I AM, SPENDING...ER, AH...QUALITY TIME WITH YOU. AND LOOK, THERE'S AN "ARLI$$" MARATHON ON TONIGHT!
MAYOR
MOST OF THESE COMICS ARE WORTHLESS AND IN TERRIBLE CONDITION...BUT SINCE YOU WERE SO THOUGHTFUL TO BRING THEM TO ME, I'D BE MORE THAN HAPPY TO GIVE YOU A FEW DOLLARS FOR YOUR EFFORTS!
HAP LITTLE ELVES
MEET ABBOTT & COSTELLO
U-UH...WHERE IS COMIC BOOK GUY AND WHAT HAVE YOU DONE WITH HIM?!
EXCELLENT WORK, STUDENT DOCTOR NICK!
HEY, EVERYBODY! I GOT AN A+!
OH, I'M SUCH A FAILURE! AND POOR! AND I HAVE NO FRIENDS!
W-W-WON'T BE LONG NOW T-T-TILL MY TAB'S P-P-PAID IN FULL AT MOE'S! SURE COULD USE A D-D-D-DRINK, BUT MUST ST-STAY STRONG UNTIL MY D-D-D-DEBT IS GONE!

KRUSTY'S RACE FOR THE CURE
HEY HEY! WE HAVE A WINNER! AND TO PRESENT THE TROPHY, HERE'S THE CURE'S LEAD SINGER...ROBERT SMITH.
YES! I'M THE BEST! THIS IS THE GREATEST DAY OF MY LIFE!
0802
WAY TO GO, HOMIE!
LOOKIN' GOOD, HOMER!
I'M SWEATIN' JUST WATCHIN' YOU!
AW, CRIPES! IF I'D KNOWN HOMER HAD A CHANCE IN HELL AT WINNING THIS THING, I WOULDN'T HAVE PUT FIVE BENJIES ON THE ETHIOPIAN!
WHERE ARE YOU GOING, SWEETHEART? I THOUGHT WE WERE GOING TO...ER, AH...SPEND THE AFTER-NOON ORGANIZING MY SASHES BY COLOR AND ELECTORIAL TERM!
SORRY, JOE, I CAN'T... I FORGOT THAT I HAVE A THING WITH...UH...YOU KNOW WHO AT... ERMM...THAT ONE PLACE. YOU GO AHEAD. I'LL BE HOME LATE, DON'T WAIT UP FOR ME!
AYE, CARUMBA! WHAT THE HECK HAPPENED IN HERE?
COMIC BOOK GUY IS SO NICE THAT HE CAN'T SAY NO TO ANYONE WHO WANTS TO SELL HIM THEIR COMICS, TOYS, OR ANYTHING ELSE!
507
...DON'T WORRY THAT YOU PUT BOOGERS ON THE KNIVES OF YOUR "STAB 'EM, JAB 'EM JAILBOTS" TOY. I'LL BE HAPPY TO REMOVE THEM MYSELF.
JAILBOTS LIKE TO SHIV MY NOSE!
...FURTHERMORE, DEAN, THIS STUDENT HAS SCORED PERFECTLY ON EVERY EXAM, AND I FEEL THAT WE SHOULD ACCELERATE HIS CURRICULUM.
IF HE CONTINUES IN THIS MANNER, HE WILL BECOME THE FIRST STUDENT IN MEDICAL SCHOOL HISTORY TO GRADUATE IN SIX MONTHS TIME!
DONE!
SO YOU'RE SAYING I'M ACTUALLY A MEDICAL GENIUS? WOW! WHO KNEW?
DEAN
THAT'S THE LAST OF THE MONEY YOU OWE, BARNEY...YOU DID IT! YOU PAID OFF YOUR ENTIRE TAB!
AND I'M COMPLETELY SOBER, TOO!
I GUESS I'VE GOT TO FIND SOMETHING TO DO WITH ALL THIS EXTRA MONEY AND ENERGY--
GOT TOO MUCH EXTRA MONEY AND ENERGY? WHY NOT GIVE IT BACK TO THE UNIVERSE FROM WHICH YOU WERE CREATED? JOIN US AT THE CHURCH OF SCIENTRICKERY, JUST OFF ROUTE 4 NEAR LARD LAD'S...

SIX MONTHS LATER...
KENT BROCKMAN "LIVE" ON THE SCENE TO PRESENT THIS YEAR'S "FITTEST MAN IN SPRINGFIELD" AWARD TO NONE OTHER THAN HOMER J. SIMPSON!
FITNESS MONTHLY
AN OUTSTANDING HONOR I HAVE WON THIRTEEN TIMES MYSELF, HOMER.
IN LIGHT OF YOUR TREMENDOUS ACHIEVEMENTS, I AM OFFERING YOU THE FULL-TIME JOB OF BEING MY PERSONAL TRAINER.
WOO-HOO! YOUR OPTIMUM FITNESS WILL COME BEFORE NOTHING ELSE IN MY LIFE!
DIVORCE PAPERS?! YOU CAN'T LEAVE ME IN THE MIDDLE OF AN ELECTION! THE PEOPLE OF SPRINGFIELD WON'T ELECT SOMEONE WHO'S A FAILURE IN HIS PERSONAL LIFE! I NEED YOU!
QUIMBY!
MAYOR
VOTE
I'M SORRY, JOE, BUT AFTER SPENDING SO MUCH TIME WITH YOU THESE PAST FEW MONTHS, I REALIZE THAT I JUST DON'T LOVE YOU ANYMORE.
HEAVENS TO MURGATROID...MY GLORIOUS SHOP! WHO DID THIS?
THE BLAZE STARTED BECAUSE OF A FAULTY ELECTRICAL OUTLET,
BUT THE FIRE COULD HAVE BEEN PREVENTED IF THERE WASN'T SO MUCH FLAMMABLE STUFF IN THE SHOP.
HI, EVERYBODY...WELCOME TO MY NEW CLINIC! I OFFER THE LOWEST PRICES FOR THE QUICKEST RESULTS IN ALL OF SPRINGFIELD!
PLUS, I HAVE AN ACTUAL MEDICAL DEGREE NOW, SO EVERYTHING I DO ISN'T JUST A GUESS ANYMORE!
AND NOW THAT YOU HAVE GIVEN YOUR WEEKLY EARNINGS TO THE CHURCH, IT IS TIME TO OFFER SACRIFICE TO THE GODDESS BARBARELLA IN THE FORM OF THIS PHILLY CHEESE STEAK WITH EXTRA ONIONS, JUST THE WAY SHE LIKES IT.
♪ EXTRA ONIONS... ♪

DECEMBER 31ST...
...I'M SORRY, MARGE, BUT RAINIER'S NEW MOVIE STARTS SHOOTING MONDAY IN A REMOTE AREA OF ANTARCTICA AND I HAVE TO FLY OUT FIRST THING IN THE MORNING.
BUT IT'S NEW YEAR'S EVE, HOMER...WHAT ABOUT THE KIDS? WHAT ABOUT ME? WHO'S GOING TO TAKE CARE OF US?
YOU'LL BE FINE. I'LL ONLY BE GONE FOR EIGHT MONTHS. AND WITH ALL YOUR FREE TIME, MAYBE YOU CAN GET IN SHAPE, TOO.
CONGRATULATION
MY FELLOW SPRINGFIELDIANS, I THANK YOU FOR YOUR CONFIDENCE IN ME AND PROMISE TO LEAD OUR FAIR CITY TO NEW HEIGHTS.
FOR MY FIRST OFFICIAL ACT AS MAYOR, I WILL DO AWAY WITH THE MAYORIAL SASH AND REPLACE IT WITH A FINE SATIN ASCOT!
MAYOR
UNEMPLO
HAW HAW!
HI-DIDDILY-HO, KIND VAGRANT! THOUGHT YOU MIGHT LIKE THESE USED COPIES OF MY BOYS' GRAPHIC NOVEL, "300...WAYS TO SPREAD THE GOSPEL!"
WILL WORK 4 COMICS
I'M SORRY, APU, BUT I CAN'T SEE YOUR CHILDREN ANYMORE. MY OFFICES ARE CLOSED FOR GOOD AS OF TODAY, SO I SUGGEST YOU GO SEE DR. NICK.
FOR LEASE!
BUT HIS CLINIC IS TOO BUSY FROM HAVING PUT EVERY OTHER DOCTOR IN SPRINGFIELD OUT OF BUSINESS! MY CHILDREN WILL NOT BE GETTING IN FOR EXAMINATION FOR AT LEAST TWO MONTHS!
...SO YOU'RE SURE YOU DON'T WANT TO COME PARTY WITH US? IT'S NEW YEAR'S EVE, BARN!
I'M SORRY, BUT AT THE STROKE OF MIDNIGHT, I WILL HITCH A RIDE TO HEAVEN TO MEET MY MAKER ON THE TAIL OF ACE FREHLEY'S COMET. YOU ARE WELCOME TO JOIN ME.
EH, MAYBE SOME OTHER TIME. BUT IF YOU CHANGE YOUR MIND, WE'LL BE AT MOE'S.

MEANWHILE, AT THE SIMPSON HOME...
KNOCK! KNOCK!
WHO IS IT?
IT'S PROFESSOR FRINK! HAPPY NEW YEAR'S EVE, SIMPSONS!
WHAT DO YOU WANT? DID YOU COME BY TO MAKE OUR LIVES EVEN MORE MISERABLE?
I'M SIMPLY HERE TO ASK YOU ALL TO VOLUNTEER TO GIVE TESTIMONY TO THE NOBEL PRIZE AWARD COMMITTEE ABOUT HOW MY RESOLUTION KEEPER 3000 HAS MADE YOUR LIVES SO MUCH BET--
WAIT! DID YOU JUST SAY YOUR LIVES ARE MISERABLE, TOO?!
I THOUGHT MY INVENTION WOULD IMPROVE LIVES, THAT I WAS HELPING PEOPLE BETTER THEMSELVES...BUT EVERYONE WHO WAS EXPOSED TO THE MACHINE IS WORSE OFF THAN BEFORE!
SO YOU'RE SAYING A MACHINE CAUSED OUR DAD TO TURN INTO A FITNESS FREAK WHO DOESN'T CARE ABOUT US ANYMORE?
CORRECT, AS WELL AS ALTERING THE LIVES OF COMIC BOOK GUY, FORMER MAYOR QUIMBY, DR. NICK RIVIERA, AND BARNEY GUMBLE ≷NG-HEY!≷
EVERYONE HAS SUCH A HARD TIME KEEPING THEIR NEW YEAR'S RESOLUTIONS...I THOUGHT I WAS DOING THEM ALL A FAVOR.
WELL, MAYBE THE REASON PEOPLE DON'T FOLLOW THROUGH ON THEIR RESOLUTIONS IS THAT THEY'RE LAZY...OR MAYBE THEY JUST WANT TO STAY THE WAY THEY ARE.
YOU'RE A WISE YOUNG MAN, BART. I'M SORRY I HURT YOU AND YOUR FAMILY. I RESOLVE NEVER TO CREATE ANOTHER STUPID INVENTION EVER AGAIN!
NOT SO FAST, PROFESSOR! IF YOU STILL HAVE THAT MACHINE, MAYBE THERE'S A WAY TO REVERSE THE EFFECT SO THAT EVERYONE WILL RETURN TO NORMAL?!
THAT JUST MIGHT WORK! IF I REVERSE THE IONIZATION FIELD, INCREASE RADIATION WAVES, SUBLIMATE TEMPORAL REACTORS, CARRY THE THREE, FACTOR 2 SQUARED OVER X--
ENOUGH NERD TALK! WE NEED TO ACT FAST! BUT HOW DO WE GET EVERYONE IN THE SAME PLACE AT THE SAME TIME??
WITH THESE! LET'S GET TO WORK, BOYS!
64

I HOPE MY FRIENDS AT THE CHURCH OF SCIENTRICKERY LET ME BRING MY AWARD ALONG ON OUR TRIP TONIGHT!
WHAT DO YOU MEAN YOUR AWARD?!
CONGRATULATIONS.
YOU HAVE BEEN CHOSEN AS
"SPRINGFIELD'S CITIZEN OF THE YEAR."
PLEASE COME TO PLANET HYPE TONIGHT TO ACCEPT YOUR AWARD AT MIDNIGHT.
CORDIALLY, MAYOR BURNS
I'M THE ONE THEY CHOSE AS CITIZEN OF THE YEAR!
NO, I AM! LOOK, MY INVITATION "CORDIALLY" SAYS SO!
WE HAVE THE EXACT SAME INVITATION, AND UNLESS MY EYES DECEIVE ME, BOTH ARE DRAWN IN FIREHOUSE RED AND BURNT UMBER TONES...STAPLE COLORS OF A 64 COLOR WAXOLA CRAYON BOX!
DOES THAT MEAN WE HAVE TO SHARE THE AWARD?
NO, SIMPLETON, IT MEANS SOMEONE HAS OBVIOUSLY DUPED US INTO COMING HERE WITH THE SAME PROSPECT OF BEING CROWNED WITH SPRINGFIELD'S HIGHEST HONOR!
AND I HAVE A FEELING WE'RE ABOUT TO FIND OUT JUST WHO THAT IS...
NOT YOU TOO!
WHAT IN THE NAME OF ALVAR HANSO IS GOING ON HERE?!
YOU'RE HERE SO WE CAN GIVE YOU BACK YOUR OLD LIVES!

LISA?! ARE YOU SAYING YOU TRICKED US INTO COMING HERE FOR NO GOOD REASON?
WAIT, DOES THIS MEAN I'M NOT WINNING ANY AWARD TONIGHT?
ON THE CONTRARY, DAD... I BROUGHT YOU HERE FOR THE BEST REASON OF ALL! TO REVERSE THE SPELL SCIENCE HAS CAST ON EACH OF YOU THIS PAST YEAR, WHICH HAS MADE ALL OF OUR LIVES WORSE!
YOU SEE, PROFESSOR FRINK EXPOSED YOU ALL TO HIS RESOLUTION KEEPER 3000 LAST NEW YEAR'S EVE, BUT IT DIDN'T CHANGE YOUR LIVES FOR THE BETTER, IT DID THE EXACT OPPOSITE.
GLA-HOVEEN! YOUNG LISA IS CORRECT. NOW, IF YOU ALL JUST STAND STILL FOR A FEW SECONDS, I'LL HAVE YOU BACK TO NORMAL AND HAPPY ONCE MORE.
I DON'T WANT MY OLD LIFE BACK! I'M A REAL DOCTOR NOW WHO TAKES CARE OF EVERY PERSON IN SPRINGFIELD IN THE QUICKEST, CHEAPEST MANNER POSSIBLE!
I CAN CRUSH ACORNS WITH MY TOES! THERE'S NOTHING THAT CAN MAKE ME GIVE THAT UP!
AND I GAVE UP DRINKING TO DONATE EVERY DOLLAR I MAKE TO A CHURCH WHO BELIEVES TROLLS LIVE IN MY MIND AND GIVE ME HEAD-ACHES!
YOU COULDN'T PAY ME TO FORFEIT MY FAITH IN SUCH A ROCK-SOLID ORGANIZATION!
ACTUALLY, I WOULDN'T MIND CHANGING THE EVENTS OF THIS PAST YEAR...
I SECOND THIS...ER, AH...CHUBBY NERD'S SENTIMENT!
WAIT! EVEN IF YOUR LIFE PERSONALLY IS BETTER, IT'S AFFECTED THE LIVES OF PEOPLE AROUND YOU IN A NEGATIVE WAY!

DAD, YOU NEVER SPEND ANY TIME WITH US NOW BECAUSE YOU'RE ALWAYS WORKING OUT OR TRAVELING THE WORLD.
DR. NICK, YOUR PRACTICE HAS BECOME SO POPULAR NO ONE IN SPRINGFIELD CAN ACTUALLY SCHEDULE AN APPOINTMENT AND MORE PEOPLE ARE BEING HURT BY THAT THAN TREATED.
AND BARNEY, YOU'RE GIVING ALL OF YOUR MONEY TO A **RELIGIOUS GROUP** THAT MEASURES FAITH BY THE SIZE OF YOUR BANK ACCOUNT!
DON'T YOU UNDERSTAND? YOU DIDN'T NEED TO **CHANGE** TO BECOME **BETTER PEOPLE**...IT'S THE PEOPLE AROUND YOU WHO **BRING OUT THE BEST** IN YOU.
HUH. I GUESS WHEN SHE PUTS IT LIKE THAT...
MAYBE WE **HAVE** BEEN WRONG THIS PAST YEAR. MAYBE WE WERE **PERFECT** JUST THE WAY WE WERE.
NUTS TO THAT! I'M STAYING THIS WAY **FOREVER**!
KRACK! BLAM! KRUNCH!
NOOOOOOO!!!

LISA...LISA? ...LISA!!
LISA! WAKE UP! IT'S ALMOST MIDNIGHT!
W-WHAT ARE YOU TALKING ABOUT? DIDN'T DAD JUST DESTROY PROFESSOR FRINK'S RESOLUTION MACHINE?
TEN...NINE... EIGHT...SEVEN...
"RESOLUTION MACHINE?!" LIS, PROFESSOR FRINK ISN'T HERE! IT'S NEW YEAR'S EVE, AND YOU FELL ASLEEP!
THEN EVERY-THING'S BACK TO NORMAL! EVERYONE'S STILL LEADING THEIR BORING OLD LIVES?!
SIX...FIVE... FOUR...THREE....
I DON'T KNOW WHAT YOU'RE TALKING ABOUT, BUT YOU MUST'VE HAD SOME CRAZY DREAM!
HERE! GET READY FOR THE TOAST!
TWO... ONE...
HAPPY NEW YEAR!
OH, DAD, I'M SO GLAD YOU'RE STILL YOU! PLEASE DO ME A FAVOR AND NEVER KEEP ANY OF YOUR NEW YEAR'S RESOLUTIONS!
DON'T BE SILLY, HONEY! I NEVER HAVE, AND I NEVER WILL!
THE END

HAVE A BLAST

WITH THESE GREAT SIMPSONS BOOKS!

ISBN: 9781852865979

ISBN: 9781852866693

ISBN: 9781852867270

ISBN: 9781852867645

ISBN: 9781852868062

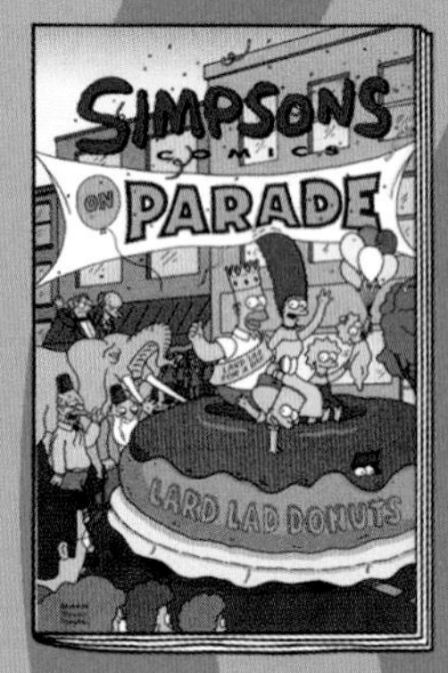

ISBN: 9781852869557

ISBN: 9781840230581

ISBN: 9781840231519

ISBN: 9781840234039

ISBN: 9781840235920

ISBN: 9781840237900

ISBN: 9781845760106

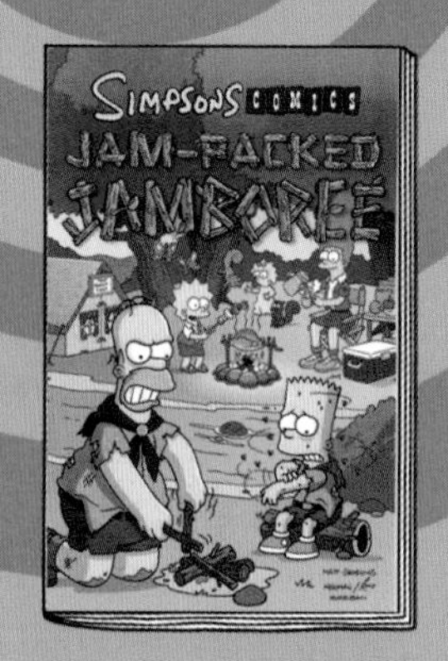

ISBN: 9781845762285

ISBN: 9781845764104

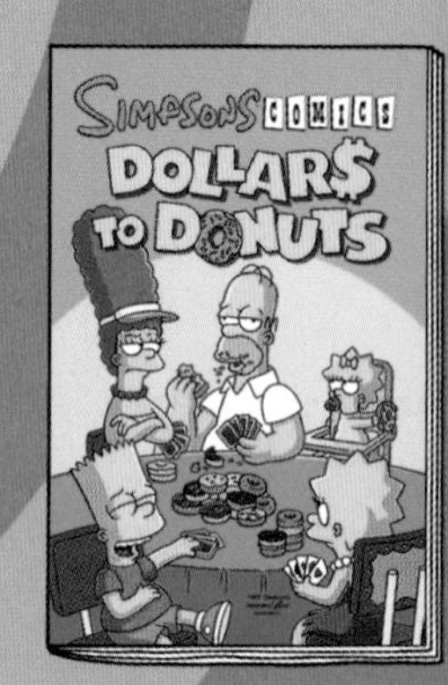

ISBN: 9781845767518

ISBN: 9781848562271

ISBN: 9781852868208

ISBN: 9781848565197

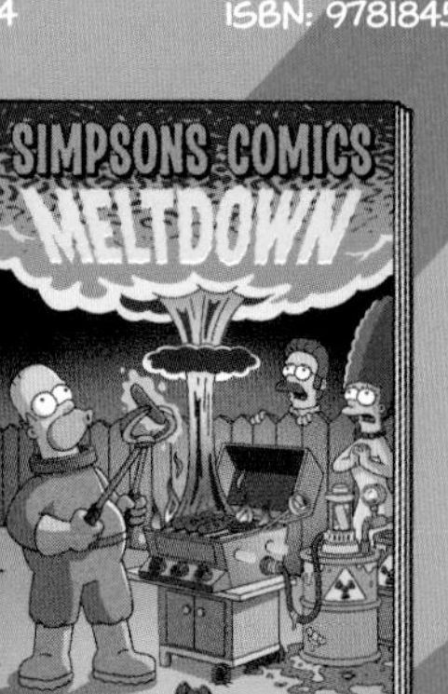

ISBN: 9780857681560

WWW.TITANBOOKS.COM

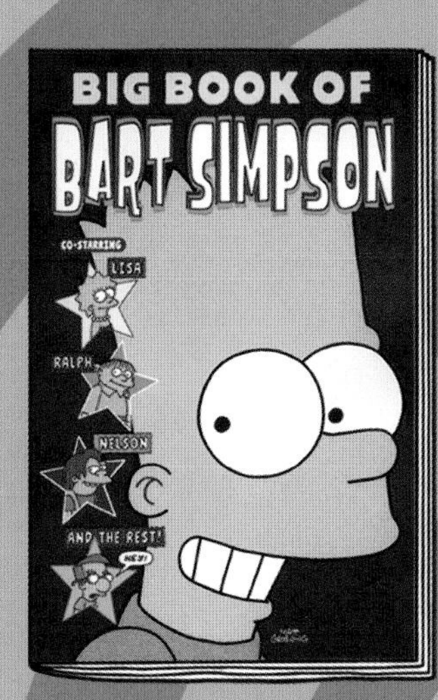

ISBN: 9781840234251

ISBN: 9781840236545

ISBN: 9781840238464

ISBN: 9781845760571

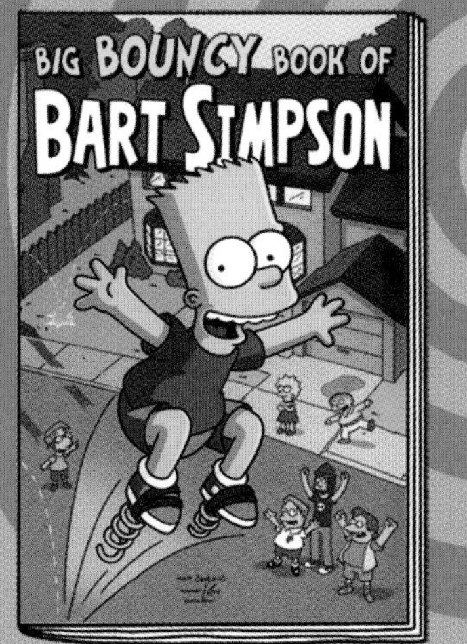

ISBN: 9781845763046

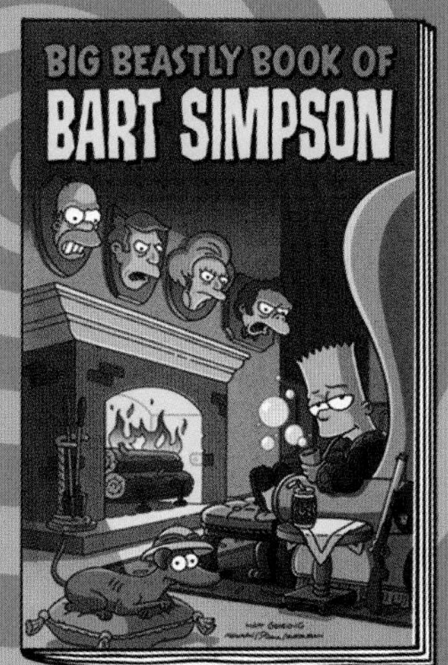

ISBN: 9781845764111

BIG BRILLIANT BOOK OF BART SIMPSON

ISBN: 9781845767525

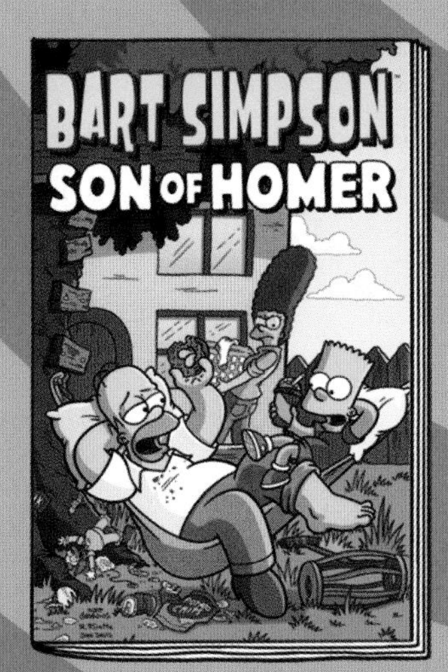

ISBN: 9781848562288

ISBN: 9781848567504

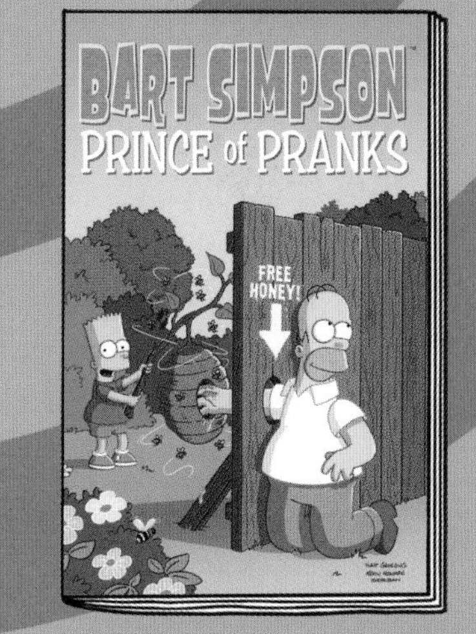

ISBN: 9780857681492

MATT GROENING

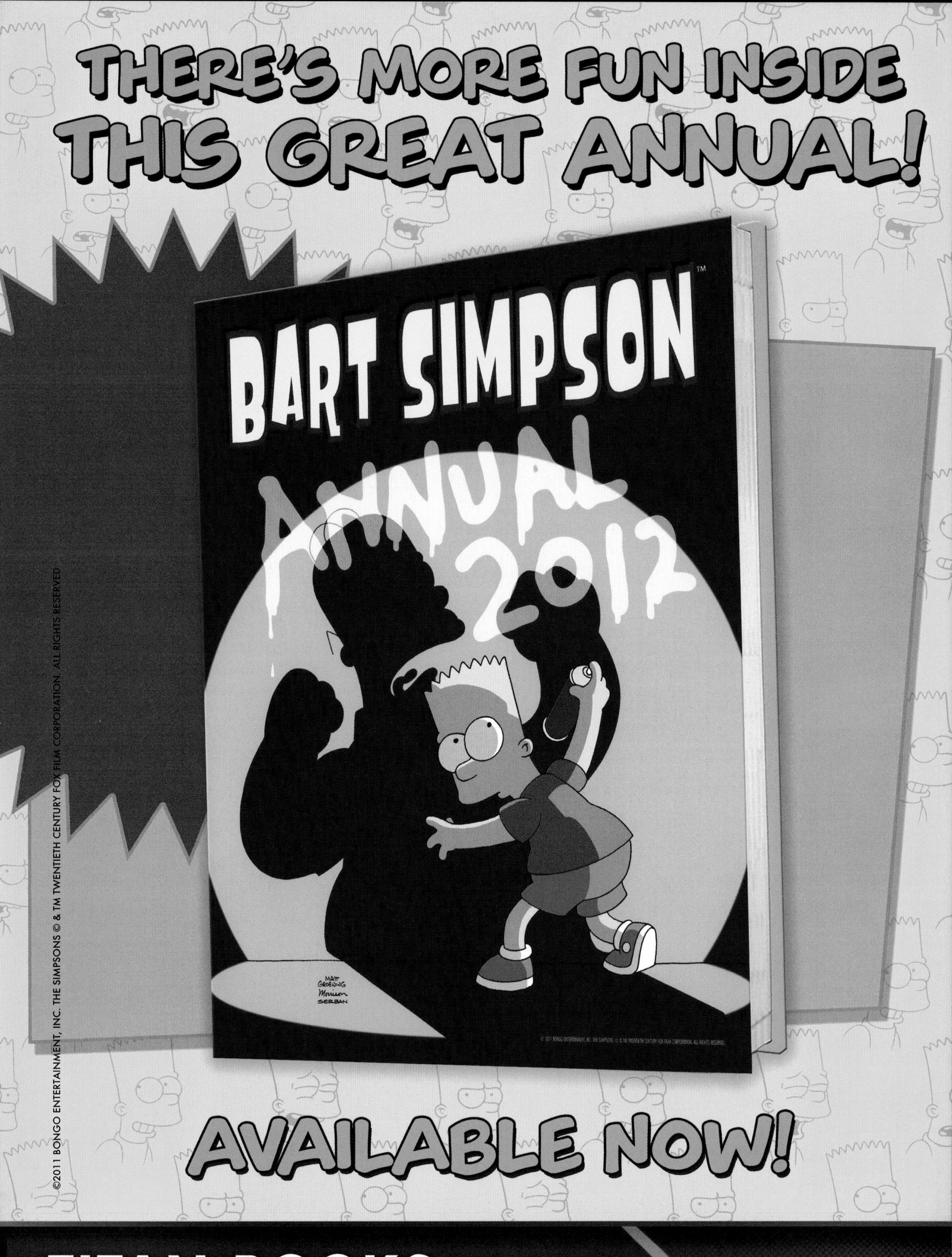
THERE'S MORE FUN INSIDE
THIS GREAT ANNUAL!
BART SIMPSON
ANNUAL 2012
AVAILABLE NOW!

TITAN BOOKS
A WORLD OF ENTERTAINMENT

MMM... COMICS!
SIMPSONS COMICS PRESENTS
THE SIMPSONS
THE DEATH OF... COMIC BOOK GUY
GUEST-STARRING STAN "THE MAN" LEE!
FIRST ISSUE! 1
BRAND NEW EPIC 3-PART STORY!
FREE GIFT WITH EVERY ISSUE!
SUPER-SIZED SUMMER SPECIAL!
SIMPSONS COMICS SUMMER SHINDIG
#188
FREE INFLATABLE BALL!
BART! SUMMER BOY
MAGGIE! RAY OF SUNSHINE
LISA! SUPER-SIZED
FREE GIFT WITH EVERY ISSUE!
FUTURAMA COMICS
#61
SUMMER 2011 NO. 61 £2.99
SUBSCRIBE TODAY AND SAVE UP TO 15%!
MATT GROENING